ROGER MELLIE
THE MAN ON THE TELLY

ROGER?.. TOM!.. LISTEN, GOOD NEWS. YOU'VE BEEN ASKED TO HOST THIS YEAR'S 'DAILY POST' CHILDREN OF BRAVERY AWARDS AT THE SAVOY...

YEAH!?

IT'S A REALLY GOOD CAUSE AND THINK OF THE EXPOSURE.

..THEY'LL ALL BE THERE, ROGER- TARBY, BRUCIE, WOGAN, EAMON HOLMES.

SOUNDS LIKE A GOOD GIG TO ME, TOM... WHAT'S THE PURSE?

THE PURSE? WELL... THERE'S NO FEE AS SUCH... THE HONOUR IS ITS OWN REWARD, ROGER!

HMM!

THESE KIDS HAVE DONE AMAZING THINGS, ROGER, RESCUING PEOPLE FROM FIRES AND SUCH...

HMM!

CALLING AMBULANCES FOR PEOPLE...Y'KNOW

WHAT ABOUT EX-IES, TOM?

WELL...ER...

...YOU'LL BE ABLE TO CLAIM A FEW EXPENSES, I SUPPOSE

WELL COUNT ME IN...I'M A FUCKIN' ARTIST WHEN IT COMES TO CLAIM FORMS... A BLANK EXPENSE SHEET IS MY CANVAS, TOM.

I ONCE DID A THREE MINUTE PIECE ABOUT A SKATEBOARDING TOAD FOR NATIONWIDE IN 1978... AN OVER-NIGHT STOP IN THE HOLIDAY INN, HULL...

CLAIMED EIGHT GRAND

SO YOU'LL DO IT, THEN?

YOU KNOW ME... ANYTHING FOR LITTLE KIDDIES

GREAT! IT'S NEXT TUESDAY AT 8:00

TUESDAY? SORRY, TOM. NO CAN DO

BUT, ROGER...WHAT ABOUT THE LITTLE KIDDIES?

FUCK 'EM, TOM!

I'M KEEPING MY EVENINGS OPEN NEXT WEEK... PAXMAN'S OFF FISHING FOR A WEEK SO THE NEWSNIGHT CHAIR IS UP FOR GRABS

...IT'S AS GOOD AS PROMISED TO ME, TOM...I'M GOING TO SEE THE PRODUCER THIS AFTERNOON...

JUST THE FORMALITIES

... I'LL POP INTO THE OFFICE ON MY WAY BACK

LATER...   OH, HI, ROGER...

HOW DID IT GO? WHEN DO YOU START?

I DON'T

THEY ONLY GAVE THE FUCKING JOB TO DICK AND DOM

DICK AND DOM? ...NEWSNIGHT?

SOME OLD BOLLOCKS ABOUT CURRENT AFFAIRS GOING FOR A YOUNGER AUDIENCE

WELL, IT'S HAPPENING ALL THROUGH THE MEDIA, ROGER

YOU'RE TELLING ME, TOM... LOOK AT THIS..

...'PANORAMA, PRESENTED BY VERNON KAYE'... I ASK YOU, TOM

VERNON FUCKING KAYE!

AND HERE...'THE SKY AT NIGHT WITH CAT DEELEY'... I MEAN, FOR FUCK'S SAKE!

THEY'RE TURNING TELLY INTO A KIDS GAME, TOM. THERE'S NO ROOM FOR PROS LIKE ME ANY MORE

HMM!

WELL I'M NOT GOING TO TAKE IT LYING DOWN, TOM, NO. I'VE BOOKED MYSELF IN FOR A BIT OF THE OLD NIP 'N' TUCK

PLASTIC SURGERY?

TOO RIGHT! I'M UNDER THE KNIFE TOMORROW... FACE LIFT, CHIN TUCK, NOSEJOB, LIPOSUCTION... THE FULL ANNE ROBINSON

NOT MUCH CHANGE FROM FORTY GRAND, TOM

FORTY GRAND? WHERE WILL YOU GET FORTY GRAND FROM?

THE KIDDIES BRAVERY AWARDS GIG, TOM...

...HERE...

?

... I'VE ALREADY FILLED MY EXPENSE CLAIM FORM OUT

A WEEK LATER

WELL, THE AWARDS WENT VERY WELL I THOUGHT

VERY WELL?

YOU FRIGHTENED HALF THE CHILDREN TO DEATH, ROGER!

I THOUGHT THE LITTLE SODS WERE SUPPOSED TO BE BRAVE

BUT ROGER... YOU LOOK LIKE FRANKENSTEIN'S MONSTER.

HEY! THIS HAS PUT ANOTHER 30 YEARS ON MY CAREER, TOM ...I'LL JUST NIP FOR PISS.

YOU SHOULD HAVE IT DONE, TOM...CAN'T FEEL A THING, Y'KNOW...

I DON'T THINK SO, ROGER

THEY JUST GET ALL THE LOOSE SKIN, PULL IT UP REALLY TIGHT, CUT OFF THE EXCESS AND SEW IT UP UNDER YOUR EARS...

...MY EXPENSES CAME THROUGH FOR THAT AMNESTY INTERNATIONAL DINNER I DID, SO I COULD LEND YOU THE CASH

PSSSS!

Viz

The
Roger Mellie Telly Times

A Collection of the Best Adventures
Featuring Fulchester TV's Lead Anchorman
Roger Mellie OBE

Written and Drawn by
Simon Thorp and Graham Dury

Additional material by Chris Donald, Simon Donald, Davey Jones and Alex Collier

ISBN 978-1-78106-372-9

Dennis Publishing Ltd., 30 Cleveland Street, London W1T 4JD

First Printing Autumn 2015

Printed in the United Kingdom

Subscribe online at www.viz.co.uk

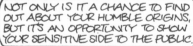

...A TEAR, TOM? YOU WANT ME TO BLUB?

YES, ROGER... IT'S GREAT P.R.

JEREMY PAXMAN CRIED OVER HIS GREAT GRANNY AND THE VIEWING FIGURES FOR NEWSNIGHT WENT THROUGH THE ROOF!

GOTCHA, TOM... SO WHO'S THIS CUNT AGAIN?

HE'S YOUR GREAT GRANDFATHER, ROGER... JOSIAH MELLIE

RUFFLE! RUFFLE! RUFFLE!

OKAY... THREE... TWO... ONE...

ACTION!

AH! HERE WE GO... JOSIAH MELLIE

DIED OF DYSENTERY... DECEMBER 25th, 1861... FULCHESTER POOR HOUSE

...AGE... ...31...

...31... DEAR, DEAR.

31

TUT! TUT!

PHEW!

SNIFF!

...31...

CUT!

SORRY, TOM, I CAN'T SQUEEZE ONE OUT... CAN YOU SEND A RUNNER TO THE SHOP FOR AN ONION?

DON'T WORRY, ROGER... WE'LL SHOOT ROUND IT... WE'LL PUT THE CAMERA BEHIND YOUR HEAD AND DROP SOME WATER ON THE DEATH CERTIFICATE... LET THE INK RUN A BIT...

...A FEW POIGNANT PIANO CHORDS IN THE BACKGROUND... NOBODY WILL BE ANY THE WISER

I DON'T KNOW, TOM, COME TO THINK OF IT. IS THERE NOBODY MORE INTERESTIN' IN MY FAMILY TREE THAN THIS TWAT?

I MEAN, WHO WANTS TO HEAR ABOUT SOME VICTORIAN TRAMP SHITTING HIMSELF TO DEATH IN THE WORKHOUSE ON CHRISTMAS DAY?..

NOBODY...

...PEOPLE WANT TO HEAR ABOUT SUCCESS, TOM

CAN'T WE FIND SOME OF MY FOLK WITH A BIT MORE PIZZAZZ?

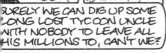
SURELY WE CAN DIG UP SOME LONG LOST TYCOON UNCLE WITH NOBODY TO LEAVE ALL HIS MILLIONS TO, CAN'T WE?

BE TV GOLD THAT WOULD TOM... JUST IMAGINE THE EMOTION WHEN WE MEET FOR THE FIRST TIME

HMM!

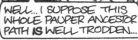
WELL... I SUPPOSE THIS WHOLE PAUPER ANCESTOR PATH IS WELL TRODDEN...

EXACTLY, TOM. IT MIGHT BE NICE TO FIND SOME MORE RECENT, SUCCESSFUL RELATIONS

HEY, SWEET TITS... GET BACK TO LOOKING THROUGH ALL THIS LOT AGAIN, WILL YOU?

GIVE ME A SHOUT WHEN YOU FIND SOME MELLIES WITH A FEW BOB IN THEIR BACK BINS

A WEEK LATER...

WELCOME TO FTV

HI, TOM. ANY LUCK?

AH, ROGER, YES! THE RESEARCHER HAS BEEN DOING SOME DIGGING...

...TURNS OUT YOU'VE GOT QUITE AN EXTENSIVE FAMILY.

THEY'RE DYING TO MEET YOU, ROGER

ARE THEY TALKING MONEY, TOM?

REALLY?

YES. YOU'VE GOT RELATIVES YOU NEVER KNEW YOU HAD ALL OVER THE COUNTRY

ERM... YES, I THINK THEY ARE, ROGER

GREEN ROOM

GOOD AFTERNOON, MR MELLIE... I'M FROM THE CHILD SUPPORT AGENCY...

C.S.A.

SUNDAY...

ROGER! ROGER!

ROGER! HAVE YOU SEEN THE PAPERS?

NO, TOM...

WHAT HAVE THEY CAUGHT ME DOING **THIS** TIME?... COCAINE AGAIN...OR MORE PROSTITUTES?... OR BOTH?

NO, ROGER...THEY SAY YOU'VE GOT PAID NINE GRAND FOR PRESENTING FTV'S **NEEDY KIDDIES** TELETHON

NO, TOM

WHAT!?

YES. AND THEY SAY YOU'VE BEEN PAID NINE GRAND FOR DOING IT EVERY YEAR SINCE 1980

NEWS OF THE World BOO! HISS! TV MELLIE AID 9K FOR CHARITY SHOW

WIN SOME BIG TITS

NO, TOM... THERE'S BEEN SOME SORT OF MISTAKE

I MEAN, DO I LOOK LIKE THE KIND OF BLOKE WHO'D TAKE **9 GRAND** FOR DOING A KIDDIES CHARITY SHOW

I'M GOIN' TO HAVE TO SPEAK TO MY AGENT ABOUT THIS, TOM

HELLO?...

...IT'S ROGER...

...YES, I **HAVE** FUCKIN' SEEN IT

...YOU LOOK AT MY FUCKIN' CONTRACT

IT'S **NINETEEN** GRAND A SHOW, YOU TWAT, NOT NINE...NINETEEN

JESUS, THIS COULD RUIN MY REPUTATION, Y'KNOW. PEOPLE WILL THINK I WORK FOR FUCKIN' **PEANUTS**

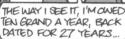

THE WAY I SEE IT, I'M OWED TEN GRAND A YEAR, BACK DATED FOR 27 YEARS...

...THAT'S 270 GRAND THEY OWE ME, SO YOU GET IT FUCKIN' **SORTED**!

A WEEK LATER...

SAY CHEESE

FLASH!

NEEDY KIDDIES APPEAL PAY ROGER MELLIE TWO HUNDRED AND £270,000 SEVENTY THOUSAND POUNDS ONLY

SO, THE TEN CANDIDATES ARE WAITING TO MEET YOU IN THE BOARDROOM, ROGER...

YOUR JOB IS TO SET THEM TASKS TO SEE HOW THEY WORK AS A **TEAM**... AND TO SEE IF ANY OF THEM HAVE LEADERSHIP QUALITY

EACH WEEK YOU BRING THEM ALL BACK INTO THE BOARDROOM... AND **SACK** ONE OF THEM...

GOTCHA, TOM

...ONE WHO HAS BEEN PARTICULARLY WEAK, OR WHO HAS DISPLAYED ANY BAD BUSINESS ACUMEN...OKAY?

YOU WEED THEM OUT WEEK BY WEEK, ROGER, SO THAT AFTER **10** SHOWS THERE'S ONLY ONE LEFT...

...THAT'S THE ONE WHO GETS THE JOB AS YOUR APPRENTICE HERE AT FULCHESTER T.V...

...BUT REMEMBER, THIS IS A **REAL** JOB THAT THEY ARE AFTER, ROGER...

...YOU ONLY WANT THE **BEST**! THE ONE WHO'S GOING TO BE AN ASSET TO FULCHESTER T.V.

EVERYONE... MAY I INTRODUCE ROGER MELLIE

HI!

HI, MR MELLIE

HI!

MR MELLIE

HI

PLEASED TO MEET YOU

HI, MR MELLIE

HI

ARE YOU SURE YOU WANT TO DO TEN SHOWS, TOM?..

ONLY, WE CAN WRAP THIS FUCKER UP TONIGHT IF Y'LIKE

ROGER MELLIE THE MAN ON THE TELLY

ONE DAY... HI, TOM. ANY SHOWS TO DO TODAY?..NO? OKAY, I'M OFF FOR A QUICK NINE HOLES AT THE TWAT FARM...

OH, ER... ACTUALLY, ROGER, THERE **IS** SOMETHING!

OH!?! WHAT'S THAT?

CLACKLE!

I'VE HAD SOMEONE ON THE PHONE. THEY'RE LOOKING FOR A PRESENTER TO STAND IN FOR TIM WESTWOOD

TIM WESTWOOD?

...ISN'T HE THAT TRENDY, YOUNG DJ

TRENDY?..WELL HIS DAD WAS THE BISHOP OF PETERBOROUGH. AND HE'S HARDLY YOUNG...

...HE'S HAVING A FEW WEEKS OFF TO HAVE HIP REPLACEMENT AND CATARACT SURGERY.

OH! ANYWAY, WHAT'S THE SHOW?

PIMP MY RIDE UK! HAVE YOU SEEN IT?

SEEN IT?... I **LOVE** IT, TOM. IT'S ONE OF MY FAVOURITE SHOWS

GREAT!... SO YOU'LL KNOW WHAT'S NEEDED

SURE!

WELL FILMING STARTS IN ONE HOUR, ROGER, AT CLIFF STREET GARAGES. DON'T BE LATE!

HAVE I EVER LET YOU DOWN, TOM?

3 HOURS LATER...

CLIFF ST.

WELL, IT LOOKS LIKE HE'S NOT COMING...WE'LL CALL IT A DAY, EVERYONE

C & S MOTORS

NO!.. HERE HE IS...

TOM, MY MAIN MAN...LET ME INTRODUCE YOU TO MY BITCHES

ARE WE GOING TO BE ON TELLY?...GIGGLE!

THIS IS BITCH ONE, AND THIS IS BITCH TWO. HEH! HEH!

ROGER...WHAT ON EARTH DO YOU THINK YOU ARE DOING?

...YOU TURN UP TWO HOURS LATE DRESSED LIKE HUGGY BEAR WITH TWO...ERM... LADIES ON YOUR ARM

I WAS PREPARING FOR THE SHOW, TOM...REMEMBER THE 'SIX **P** PRINCIPLE'..

PROPER PLANNING PREVENTS PISS-POOR PERFORMANCE...

HAVE YOU EVER SEEN 'PIMP MY RIDE'?

SURE...WE GET SOME PUNTERS TO BANG THESE PROS IN THE BACK OF A VAN WHILE YOU DRIVE IT ROUND THE RINGROAD

IT'S ON THE 'RED HOT AMATEUR CHANNEL' EVERY NIGHT AT 3:00 AM

RED HOT AMATEURS!?..NO, ROGER. IT'S A CAR RENOVATION SHOW...IT'S ON MTV

HEY, YOU'RE RIGHT, TOM...I'M THINKING OF 'UK FANNY VAN'

AH, WELL, WE WON'T BE NEEDING YOU NOW, GIRLS

'ERE! WOT 'BOUT OUR MONEY?

BUNG 'EM FIFTY QUID A PIECE, WILL Y' TOM? STICK IT ON YOUR EXXIES.

SHORTLY... RIGHT, TOM...WHERE DO I STAND? WHAT DO I SAY?

WELL, WE'RE ALMOST FINISHED, ROGER. THERE'S JUST ONE SCENE TO SHOOT.

THIS IS ZAK WHOSE FIAT PANDA HAS JUST BEEN PIMPED...JUST WALK ROUND THE CAR WITH HIM AND CHAT ABOUT WHAT'S BEEN DONE.

NO PROBLEM, TOM...LET'S GO.

AND... ACTION!

WELL, ZAK. WHAT DO YOU THINK OF YOUR SHINY NEW CAR? ISN'T IT SUPER? AND THOSE WHEELS ARE SPLENDID. AND IT'S PAINTED A LOVELY COLOUR

CUT!

PROBLEM, TOM? PLANE GOING OVER, WAS IT?

NO...IT'S YOU, ROGER...

YOU SEE, THIS IS A **YOUTH** PROGRAMME, YOU'VE GOT TO USE UP-TO-THE-MINUTE STREET LANGUAGE.

EH?

WELL, FOR EXAMPLE, DON'T SAY 'THESE WHEELS ARE SPLENDID'...YOU SAY 'THESE LOW-PROS ARE REALLY PHAT!'

FAT?

YES!...SAY 'THEY'RE HOT AND THEY REALLY PLAY THE PART'

AND THE PAINTWORK'S NOT SHINY, ROGER, IT'S **BLINGIN'**

BLINGIN?...

CHRIST ON A BIKE. I'M GETTING TOO OLD FOR THIS CAPER, TOM. BUT I'LL GIVE IT MY BEST SHOT

SO... AND... ACTION!

HEY, ZAK! WHAT IT **IS**, BRO! LET'S CHECK OUT YOUR PIMPED-UP RIDE MY FAT MAN...

YO! GET A LOAD OF THESE BLINGIN' FUNKY LOW-PROS...WOO! THEY'RE X TO THE ZEE, DUDE

?

AND EYEBALL THIS GROOVY HI-FI SYSTEM. WITH THESE BABIES PUMPIN' OUT YOUR FAVE CHOONS, YOU'LL BE ABLE TO GET ON DOWN TO THE BEAT AND STRUT YO' FUNKY STUFF EVERY TIME YOU PUT THE PEDAL TO THE METAL

THERE YOU GO, TOM. WAS THAT 'STREET' ENOUGH FOR YOU?

NEXT DAY...

HI, TOM. YOU WANTED TO SEE ME?

YES, ROGER...THIS IS FRANK WANKENSTEIN, HEAD OF MTV UK

HI!

I JUST CAME OVER TO TELL YOU ABOUT THE SHOW, ROGER...

...WE WATCHED THE TAPES AND...WELL, TO BE HONEST, YOUR PERFORMANCE WAS CRINGEWORTHY...

YOU WERE THREE TIMES OLDER THAN ANYONE ELSE ON SCREEN, YOU WERE USING WORDS YOU DIDN'T UNDERSTAND, AND YOU WERE WOODEN AND STILTED...

...IN A NUTSHELL, ROGER, YOU WERE THE IDEAL REPLACEMENT FOR TIM WESTWOOD

?

WE AT MTV LIKE YOU, ROGER...AND WE'VE GOT A PROJECT WE THINK YOU MIGHT BE INTERESTED IN...

NEXT DAY...

MTV PRODUCTIONS, OPENING TITLES... TAKE ONE!

DATE: 6/5/05 PROD: MTV
SCENE: OPENING TITLES
INC: ROGER MELLIE

CLACK!

HI! I'M ROGER MELLIE...

...AND THIS IS JACKASS UK!

FSSSS!

SEWERAGE FARM 100 YDS

THAT WAS MR. KENNEDY... HE'S LOST HIS JOB AND FALLEN BEHIND WITH HIS MORTGAGE PAYMENTS...

HE NEEDED TO BORROW £15000 TO AVOID BEING EVICTED...

I HOPE YOU TOLD HIM TO **FUCK OFF**, LOVE!

CUT!

WHAT IS IT? WAS THERE A HAIR IN THE GATE?

NO, ROGER...JUST STICK TO THE SCRIPT. YOU SAY "WERE YOU ABLE TO HELP?"...

THEN YOU JUST NOD YOUR HEAD WHILE THE TELE-PHONIST EXPLAINS HOW VERMIN LOANS HELPED.

GOTCHA! LEAVE IT TO ME OKAY. LET'S GO AGAIN...

... QUIET ON THE SET!

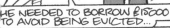

...THREE...TWO...ONE... ACTION!

WERE YOU ABLE TO HELP?

YES!

VERMIN LOANS TOOK HIS EXISTING MONTHLY OUTGOINGS AND CONSOLIDATED THEM INTO ONE MANAGEABLE PAYMENT

...AND OUR LOAN ARRANGEMENT EVEN LEFT HIM WITH £2000 CASH TO TAKE HIMSELF ON A WELL-DESERVED HOLIDAY

EH?...WHAT WAY'S **THAT** TO RUN A FUCKING BUSINESS?

CUT!

I MEAN, COME ON...

HE'S GOT NO MONEY, NO JOB AND THEY'RE SENDING HIM ON A TWO GRAND JUNKET. FUCKING MADNESS, IT IS...

I HOPE THEY'VE GOT ENOUGH TO PAY ME FOR DOING THIS.

LOOK, WE'RE PAYING BY THE HOUR TO RENT THIS PLACE... JUST GET ON AND DO YOUR LINES... JESUS!

LET'S TAKE IT FROM 'THAT WAS MR KENNEDY'

DIRECTOR

QUIET ON THE SET, EVERYONE... THREE!..TWO...ONE... ACTION!

THAT WAS MR. KENNEDY...

HE'S LOST HIS JOB AND FALLEN BEHIND WITH HIS MORTGAGE REPAYMENTS... HE NEEDED TO BORROW £15000 TO AVOID...

KENNEDY YOU SAY?

NOT **STAN** KENNEDY, WAS IT? DID HE HAVE A HIGH PITCHED SQUEAKY VOICE?.. IRISHMAN?..

CUT!

IF IT WAS, DON'T LEND HIM FUCK ALL...

OWED ME FIFTY QUID FOR YEARS

HONESTLY... KISS GOODBYE TO OWT YOU LEND HIM. PISSES EVERY PENNY UP THE WALL, STAN KENNEDY DOES...

RIGHT! LET'S FORGET IT, EH? LET'S JUST FORGET IT!

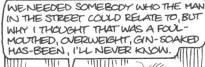

WHAT?... LOOK, I WAS ONLY TRYING TO SAVE YOU A BOB OR TWO...

YES, IT'S MY FAULT...

IT'S MY FAULT. IT WAS A MISTAKE TO BOOK YOU. WHAT WAS I THINKING?

WE NEEDED SOMEBODY WHO THE MAN IN THE STREET COULD RELATE TO, BUT WHY I THOUGHT THAT WAS A FOUL-MOUTHED, OVERWEIGHT, GIN-SOAKED HAS-BEEN, I'LL NEVER KNOW.

GET ONTO THE AGENCY, WOULD YOU, POPPY?.. SEE IF THEY'VE GOT ANYBODY MORE SUITABLE

RIGHT AWAY

OUTSIDE

WELL, ROGER... THAT 50K WOULD'VE STRAIGHTENED YOU OUT... WHAT ARE YOU GOING TO DO FOR MONEY NOW?

FULCHESTER TELESALES LTD

WELCOME TO FULCHESTER BUSINESS PARK

AH, DON'T WORRY, TOM...I'LL GET IT FROM SOMEWHERE... SOMETHING WILL TURN UP

NEXT DAY...

QUIET ON THE SET, EVERYONE... THREE... TWO...ONE...

ACTION!

DIRECTOR

HELLO. I'M BERNARD MANNING... NOW WE ALL FIND OURSELVES IN FINANCIAL DIFFICULTY EVERY NOW AND AGAIN, AND IT'S GOOD TO KNOW THAT HELP IS AT HAND...

YOU'RE WELCOME, SIR...

GOODBYE!

...AND THAT'S WHERE THOSE NICE PEOPLE AT VERMIN LOANS COME IN.

THAT WAS MR. MELLIE... HE'S BEEN OUT OF WORK FOR 8 MONTHS. HE'S GOT THREE EX-WIVES DEMANDING MONEY, AND HE OWES A FORTUNE TO THE INLAND REVENUE AND THE CHILD SUPPORT AGENCY...

HE NEEDED TO BORROW £15000 TO PAY OFF A BOOKIE'S BILL

I HOPE YOU TOLD 'IM T' **FUCK OFF**, LOVE!

CUT!

ROGER MELLIE

THE MAN ON THE TELLY

IT'S NOW EIGHT DAYS SINCE BBC REPORTER ROGER MELLIE WAS KIDNAPPED IN THE GAZA STRIP...

FREE ROGER MELLIE

...AND AS HE BEGINS HIS SECOND WEEK AS A HOSTAGE, THE CAMPAIGN FOR HIS RELEASE IS WELL UNDER WAY HERE AT TELEVISION CENTRE

SOPHIE. CAN YOU GET ON TO THE WORLD SERVICE AND SEE IF THEY CAN BROADCAST A MESSAGE ON THEIR ARABIC NETWORK?

TOBY. HAVE YOU ORDERED ALL THE STUFF FOR THE BALLOON RELEASE IN TRAFALGAR SQUARE?

SURE

DONE IT, TOM

GREAT

OH, HUGO, COULD YOU CALL THE SUPPLIERS AND SEE WHEN THE YELLOW RIBBONS ARE ARRIVING?

OKEEDOKEE

I LIKE THE T-SHIRTS, TOM. NICE IDEA... HOW MUCH ARE WE PUNTING THEM OUT FOR?

WE'RE NOT SELLING THEM, ROGER. WE'RE GOING TO HAND THEM OUT TO FOLK OUTSIDE THE PALESTINIAN...

ROGER!?!.. WHAT THE FUCK?

THESE ARE TOP QUALITY SHIRTS, TOM...

..HOW?.. I MEAN... WHAT..?

..Y'COULD GET A TENNER EACH FOR THESE... TELL YOU WHAT, I'LL SIGN A FEW AND WE'LL STICK 'EM ON EBAY

WHAT ARE YOU DOING HERE ROGER?.. I THOUGHT YOU WERE CHAINED TO A RADIATOR IN THE MIDDLE EAST...

NO, TOM... THAT WAS JUST A BIT OF SPIN

I WAS HOSTING A WET T-SHIRT CONTEST FOR BRAVO TV AT THE DUBAI HILTON WHEN I CAME UP WITH THE IDEA

IDEA?.. WHAT IDEA?

WELL... ALL OF THIS, TOM. PRETEND TO BE HELD HOSTAGE... GET A BIT OF A CAMPAIGN GOING

I GET MY PROFILE RAISED AND A JUICY BOOK DEAL, NEWS 24 AND 5 LIVE GET A BIT OF A SOAP OPERA. EVERYONE'S A WINNER

HEY, IT'S GOING TO GET GOOD NEXT WEEK, TOM... MY KIDNAPPERS CUT MY EAR OFF AND POST IT TO THE BREAKFAST NEWS TEAM...

JUST GOT TO GET HOLD OF AN EAR FROM SOMEWHERE

BUT... THE DIRECTOR GENERAL... HE'LL GO MAD WHEN HE FINDS OUT

NO, HE FUCKIN' LOVES IT, TOM

WHAT!?! HE KNOWS?

YES

I MENTIONED IT TO HIM... WE WERE ON THE SAME HONESTY TRAINING COURSE

THE 'FREE ROGER' BASEBALL HATS ARE HERE, MR MELLIE... AND HOLLY HAS JUST TAKEN ANOTHER BOX OF BADGES TO THE BBC SHOP...

...THEY'RE SELLING LIKE HOTCAKES

FUCKING HELL! IS EVERYBODY IN ON THIS FUCKING PANTOMIME?

SHOULD BE, TOM...

...DIDN'T YOU GET THE MEMO?

NO! AND I'M NOT PUTTING UP WITH THIS... I'M CALLING THE BBC BOARD OF GOVERNORS' WHISTLE BLOWER HOTLINE

TAP! TAP! TAP!

THANK YOU FOR CALLING THE BBC BOARD OF GOVERNORS' WHISTLE BLOWER HOTLINE...

THIS CALL WILL BE CHARGED AT A RATE OF £1.50/MIN AND MAY LAST FOR MORE THAN THIRTY MINUTES...

...PLEASE ASK THE BILL PAYER'S PERMISSION BEFORE...

CLICK!

WHAT DO YOU WANT ME TO DO, ROGER?

I'VE GOT JUST THE JOB, TOM

SHORTLY... AND NOW ON 'PM', THE RESULT OF TODAY'S PREMIUM RATE PHONE-IN QUIZ. WE ASKED YOU TO NAME THE CITY IN WHICH BBC JOURNALIST ROGER MELLIE IS BEING HELD HOSTAGE...

AND ON THE LINE IS OUR WINNER... TAM, FROM SCOTLAND

THE ANSWER, OF COURSE, BEIRUT

HELLO THERE, TAM

AND WHAT'S THE WEATHER LIKE TODAY, NORTH OF THE BORDER?

OCH! IT'S AFFY DRIZZLY, JOHN

...THE NOO

CHRISTMAS TV CHOICE

Your essential viewing guide to what's on the telly this Christmas Day...

9.00 *BBC 2:* **I Love Scraping the Bottom of the Barrel.** Assorted B-list celebrities pretend to remember their childhood in precise detail whilst sitting in front of a coloured backdrop.

9.00 *ITV:* **Branching Out.** Ross Kemp stars as Robson Thaw, an unconventional tree surgeon who sometimes bends the rules but always gets results.

9.30 *ITV:* **The Ross Kemp Story.** Robson Green stars as Ross Kemp in the true life story of an unconventional actor who sometimes bends the rules but always gets results.

10.00 *BBC 2:* **I Love Stuart Maconie's Opinions.** Assorted fame hungry K-list media tarts reminisce about some of Stuart Maconie's most memorable opinions on everything from Hula Hoops and Space Hoppers to Clackers and Chopper bikes.

11.30 *ITV:* **Ross Kemp vehicle.** Another fucking programme starring Ross Kemp. Details to be confirmed.

12.00 *C4:* **Escape From Cardiff.** Claudia Winkleman introduces an exciting adventure game in which two teams of whooping lycra-clad twats are given a week to attempt to get out of The Welsh capital and reach civilsation.

1.00 *ITV:* **Robson Green, QC.** Legal drama, starring Ross Kemp as John Thaw, an unconventional police astrologer who sometimes bends the rules but always gets results.

1.00 *BBC 2:* **I Love Doing These Sorts of Programmes.** Desperate attention-seeking T-list celebrities reminisce about their favourite appearances on these sorts of programmes.

1.30 *BBC 1:* **Christmas Pro-Celebrity Golf.** Bruce Forsyth, Jimmy Tarbuck and Kenny Lynch play a round of golf with three prostitutes. Introduced by Peter Allis.

2.00 *ITV:* **The weather.** With Ross Kemp.

3.00 *ITV:* **The Queens Christmas message.** The tradi-tional Christmast Day broadcast to the commonwealth, starring Ross Kemp as Elizabeth Windsor, the unconventional monarch who sometimes bends the rules but always gets results.

3.30 *BBC 2:* **I Love Not Decided at Time of Going to Press.** Tragic W-list nonenities and Jamie Theakston reminisce about something which had not been decided at time of going to press.

4.00 *Food Channel:* **Cooking for One.** Anthea Turner cooks a Stilton cheese souffle with chick pea couscous whilst a single viewer watches.

6.00 *ITV:* **Kemp it in the Family.** Hilarious sitcom by Robson Green. Ross and Martin Kemp play Martin and Ross Kemp, two divorced brothers who marry each other's ex-wives, played by Amanda Burton and John Thaw. This week, Ross pretends he has forgotten his anniversary, but Martin has secretly planned a surprise party!

9.00 *ITV:* **Search for a Kemp.** It's down to the last two finalists, Martin and Ross. Who will impress the judges the most and win 8 badly-written drama series? On the panel are John Thaw, Amanda Burton, Robson Green, Sarah Lancashire and Ross Kemp.

10.00 *ITV:* **What the Kemps Did for Us.** Adam Hart-Davis looks at the contributions to civili-sation made by the Kemps, Ross and Martin. This week, bad acting in hoarse voices.

10.30 *ITV:* **Morse.** John Thaw plays Ken Morse, an unconven-tional rostrum cameraman who sometimes bends the rules but always gets results.

11.00 *ITV:* **The Kemps - A Warning from History.** Harrowing documentary outlining the circum-stances that allowed two unversa-tile cockney baddy actors to seize power over an entire television net-work. Narrated by Ross Kemp.

12.30 *ITV:* **Carry On Kemping.** Late night saucy fun, starring Sid James as Ross Kemp and Jack Douglas as Martin Kemp.

ANY IDEAS FOR YOUR FTV XMAS SPECIAL THIS YEAR, ROGER?

OH!?

YES, TOM. IT'S CALLED LONELY THIS CHRISTMAS...

YES... ME SPENDING THE FESTIVE SEASON ON THE STREETS WITH THE HOMELESS.

WHAT A **LOVELY** IDEA, ROGER

WELL DOWN AND OUTS ARE OFTEN IGNORED...

...AND THIS TIME OF YEAR IS THE WORST IF YOU HAVEN'T GOT A ROOF OVER YOUR HEAD

I'M GOING TO BE RIGHT THERE WITH THEM, TOM... SITTING WITH THEM... TALKING TO THEM... PATTING THEIR DOGS... FINDING OUT THEIR STORIES.

WELL... THIS IS A SIDE TO YOU THAT I'VE NEVER SEEN BEFORE, ROGER.

HMM. WELL THEY'RE JUST **PEOPLE** LIKE ME AND YOU, TOM. THEY JUST NEED A SHOULDER TO CRY ON... SOMEONE TO HUG THEM AND TELL THEM THAT THINGS WILL BE OKAY. I'M GOING TO BRING THEM A LITTLE FESTIVE CHEER.

I'M **MOVED**, ROGER... HONESTLY.

IT'S GOING TO BE BITTERLY COLD OUT THERE, THOUGH, ROGER. MAKE SURE YOU KEEP WRAPPED UP WARM, WON'T YOU?

ME!?

NO... NO... I'M NOT DOING THE OUTSIDE BROADCASTS, TOM...

EH!?... BUT I THOUGHT YOU SAID...

FRANK!...

...HAVE YOU GOT A MINUTE?

TOM, THIS IS FRANK... HE'S GOING TO STAND IN FOR THE TRAMP SHOTS... YOU KNOW, WHERE I'M ACTUALLY SAT WITH ALL THE FILTHY FUCKERS...

HI, MR. TOM

I GOT HIM FROM A LOOKALIKE AGENCY... £20 AN HOUR... GOOD, ISN'T HE, TOM?

HE'LL BE CATCHING THE FUCKING FLEAS WHILE I DO THE STUDIO VOICEOVERS.

JUST A THOUGHT, TOM... SHOULD WE TAKE HIM WITH US TO AFRICA NEXT TIME WE DO COMIC RELIEF?

HE CAN DO ALL THE BOLLOCKS WITH THE VILLAGERS DIGGING THEIR WELLS AND WE CAN SPEND THE DAY BY THE HOTEL POOL

ROGER MELLIE

THE MAN ON THE TELLY
(WHO SAYS "BOLLOCKS")

ROGER IS BETWEEN JOBS...

YOU'RE WATCHING BBC1, AND NOW IT'S TIME FOR...

...CHALLENGE ANNEKA

HEY! IT'S THAT BIRD WITH THE ARSE. I WONDER WHAT THIS IS ALL ABOUT THEN

THIS WEEK WE'VE GOT 48 HOURS TO BUILD A RIDING SCHOOL FOR BLIND ORPHANS

SO FIRST OF ALL I'D BETTER GET ON THE PHONE TO THE BUILDERS

TOM?

I'VE JUST HAD A GREAT IDEA FOR A PROGRAMME!

THE NEXT DAY IN ROGER'S OFFICE...

I'VE GOT IT TOM. A BRILLIANT IDEA THAT WILL PUT MELLIEVISION PRODUCTIONS ON THE MAP!

IT'S CALLED CHALLENGE ROGER!

EACH WEEK I'M GIVEN AN EXCITING NEW CHALLENGE TO CARRY OUT WHICH WILL BENEFIT A CHARITY

BUILDING HOSPITALS, RIDING SCHOOLS FOR THE ELDERLY, YOU KNOW THE SORT OF THING.

I'LL DRIVE AROUND ORGANISING IT ALL IN A BIG YELLOW LORRY WITH 'CHALLENGE ROGER' WRITTEN ON THE SIDE. IT'LL MAKE DEAD EXCITING T.V!

I'LL ALSO NEED A TRACKSUIT. AND ONE OF THEM PORTABLE PHONES. THE EXPENSIVE ONES!

THIS IDEA. IT SOUNDS A BIT FAMILIAR... AND BESIDES, A SHOW LIKE THAT WILL COST A FORTUNE TO PRODUCE

THAT'S WHERE YOU'RE WRONG TOM!

THIS IS THE CLEVER BIT. IT'S FOR CHARITY, TOM

SO EVERYONE WORKS FOR NOTHING!

LATER...

ARE WE ALL SET ROGER? I'VE GOT THE CAMERA

WHERE'S THE LORRY?

HERE IT IS. IT'S NOT AS BIG AS I'D HAVE LIKED, BUT IT'LL DO THE JOB

CHALENGE ROGER

SO... ERM... WHAT'S THE PROGRAMME GOING TO BE ABOUT THEN, ROGER

ALENGE ROGER

HERE, I'LL SHOW YOU THE PLANS

WE'VE GOT TO BUILD A SWIMMING POOL... IN JUST 24 HOURS!

DOUBLE SIDED PLANS

HMM! THAT CERTAINLY WILL BE A CHALLENGE

THIS SWIMMING POOL. WHERE WILL IT BE? WHO IS IT FOR?

I'LL TELL YOU ALL ABOUT IT WHEN WE GET THERE TOM

SHORTLY...

RIGHT. HERE WE ARE

ROGER. THIS PLACE LOOKS FAMILIAR

THE SWIMMING POOL WILL BE GOING HERE

BUT ROGER...

...THIS IS YOUR HOUSE!

YEAH... BUT THE POOL IS FOR CHARITY TOM

YOU SEE, THE KIDS AND THE OLD FOLKS WILL BE ABLE TO USE IT...SOMETIMES

ANYWAY, LET'S GET ON WITH IT SHALL WE. WE'VE ONLY GOT 24 HOURS, REMEMBER

OKAY ROGER, READY WHEN YOU ARE

HELLO AND WELCOME TO CHALLENGE ROGER! AND WHAT A CHALLENGE WE'VE GOT THIS WEEK

SOMEHOW OR OTHER WE'VE GOT TO TRANSFORM THIS SHABBY LOOKING LAWN INTO A LUXURY SWIMMING POOL... IN JUST 24 HOURS!

AND OF COURSE IT'S ALL FOR THE KIDS, AND THE OLD FOLKS

ROGER MELLIE
THE MAN ON THE TELLY

BLIMEY! YOU'RE EARLY, ROGER!

BLIMEY, YOU'RE EARLY SIR ROGER, IF YOU DON'T MIND, TOM...

...A BIT OF RESPECT FOR MY STATUS, PLEASE

WHAT!?

OH, YES... LOOK AT THAT FUCKER... THAT'S THE ROYAL SEAL, TOM... YOU KNOW WHAT THAT MEANS

I'M SURE I'M ABOUT TO FIND OUT, ROGER

BUCKINGHAM PALACE... EH?

AND IT'S BIRTHDAY GONG TIME, TOM

BUT YOU'VE GOT AN O.B.E. ALREADY ROGER...

EXACTLY... SO IT DOESN'T TAKE EINSTEIN TO WORK OUT THIS MUST BE A PROMOTION

OH, YES. THERE'S GOING TO BE A BIT OF SWORD WAVING OVER THE MELLIE EPAULETTES, YOU MARK MY WORDS

OF COURSE, YOU WON'T HAVE TO STAND ON CEREMONY, TOM... YOU WON'T HAVE TO CALL ME SIR ROGER. JUST PLAIN 'ROGER' WILL DO...

THANK YOU

BUT HER INDOORS WILL BE MADE UP. ...LADY LING PAU SUK... FANTASTIC

SIR ROGER MELLIE... SIR ROGER MELLIE... GOT A NICE RING TO IT, HASN'T IT, TOM?..

HMM.

...SIR ROGER MELLIE, KNIGHT OF THE GRAND ORDER OF...

...THE FUCKING BASTARDS!

WHAT IS IT, ROGER?

THEY'RE TAKING MY O.B.E. OFF ME, TOM!

TAKING IT OFF YOU?.. WHY?

THAT SHOPLIFTING BUSINESS A FEW WEEKS AGO... APPARENTLY, NICKING A FEW BOTTLES OF WHISKY AND EIGHTY BENNY HEDGES FROM TESCO 'BRINGS MY AWARD INTO DISREPUTE'

WELL PARDON ME FOR FUCKING BREATHING. BUNCH OF STUCK-UP CUNTS, ALL OF 'EM.

MEANINGLESS!?. GET REAL, TOM. AN O.B.E. PUTS £500 ON WHAT A CELEB CAN CHARGE FOR A PERSONAL APPEARANCE

FORGET IT, ROGER... IT'S ABOUT TIME WE DID AWAY WITH THE HONOURS SYSTEM ANYWAY. IT'S ALL COMPLETELY MEANINGLESS

REALLY?

YES! IF YOU WANT PLAIN JEFFREY ARCHER TO CUT YOUR RIBBON, IT'S A GRAND TOPS... BUT LORD ARCHER OF PISS-FLAPS-ON-SEA OR WHATEVER HE CALLS HIMSELF... FIVE GRAND?.. SIX GRAND?.. THE SKY'S THE FUCKING LIMIT, TOM, BELIEVE ME.

I TELL YOU, WITHOUT 'O.B.E.' AFTER MY NAME I'M LESS BANKABLE THAN FUCKING JAZZY-B

JAZZY-B?.. WHO'S THAT?

NO IDEA, TOM... BUT THE CUNT'S GOT A GONG AND HE'LL BE HIGHER ON THE LIST THAN I AM WHEN DALLAS CARPETS ARE AFTER SOMEONE TO OPEN A NEW REMNANT WAREHOUSE

I WOULDN'T MIND, BUT IT'S SUCH A BUM RAP...I **DESERVE** THAT O.B.E. FOR MY CHARITY WORK IF NOTHING ELSE...I'VE LOST COUNT OF THE NUMBER OF CELEBRITY GOLF GAMES I'VE PLAYED FOR KIDDIES IN WHEELCHAIRS...

AND I'VE ONLY EVER TAKEN REASONABLE EXPENSES, TOM

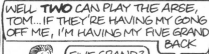

WELL **TWO** CAN PLAY THE ARSE, TOM...IF THEY'RE HAVING MY GONG OFF ME, I'M HAVING MY FIVE GRAND BACK

FIVE GRAND?

WHAT FIVE GRAND?

THE FIVE GRAND I HAD TO BUNG SOME TWAT AT MILLBANK TO GET ON THE LIST

YOU **PAID** FOR YOUR O.B.E?

WELL THAT'S WHAT O.B.E. MEANS, TOM...'OLD BROWN ENVELOPE.' HOW ELSE ARE YOU SUPPOSED TO GET ONE?

BUT THAT'S **APPALLING** ROGER

YOU'RE TELLING ME...IT'S DOWNRIGHT **THEFT!** WHEN I PAY FOR A PINT, THE LANDLORD CAN'T COME OVER AND TAKE IT BACK OFF ME

THERE SHOULD BE AN INQUIRY

I CAN'T BELIEVE YOU HANDED CASH OVER FOR AN O.B.E.

I DIDN'T, TOM... I SPONSORED A SEMINAR ON SOME SHIT AT A LABOUR CONFERENCE

...OFFICIALLY

THE LETTER FROM HER MAJ TURNED UP NEXT DAY. NOW THEY'RE TAKING IT OFF ME... THE BASTARDS

STILL, NO USE MOANING

CAMERON'S LOT HAVE GOT THEIR CONFERENCE NEXT WEEK. LET'S SEE HOW MUCH **THEY** ARE CHARGING

TAP! TAP! TAP!

HELLO!?..IS THAT THE CONSERVATIVE PARTY?... HI... ROGER MELLIE HERE...

..I'M GOOD THANKS...

...WELL, A BIT OF BAD NEWS, ACTUALLY... I'VE JUST HAD MY O.B.E. TAKEN OFF ME...

HMM...THAT'S RIGHT...THE SHOPLIFTING MIX-UP...HMM

AND I WONDERED IF YOU'D LIKE ME TO SPONSOR A SEMINAR AT YOUR PARTY CONFERENCE NEXT WEEK

SEVEN GRAND?.. THE LAST LOT ONLY CHARGED **FIVE**

YES...YES... I KNOW THEY'RE NOT IN POWER NOW...

...OKAY...SEVEN GRAND...PUT ME DOWN FOR ONE... BYE!

SEVEN GRAND, TOM...**SEVEN!** THE FUCKING ROBDOGS.

STILL...IT'LL PAY FOR ITSELF

A WEEK LATER...

MR. ROGER NATHANIEL MELLIE... ORDER OF THE BRITISH EMPIRE FOR HIS CHARITABLE WORKS AND SERVICES TO THE ENTERTAINMENT AND BROADCASTING INDUSTRIES

CONGRATULATIONS AGAIN, MR. MELLIE

THANK YOU, MA'AM

FANDABIDOZY

WAY OUT

WELL, I IMAGINE YOU HAVE HAD A MOST INTERESTING CAREER... TELL ME AB...

SORRY, I'D LOVE TO STAND ABOUT GABBING, BUT I'M OPENING A TILE WAREHOUSE IN TWENTY MINUTES

19

I'VE SEEN THE

— and they're not much to v

IT'S DIFFICULT for us to imagine that stars, just like ordinary people, use the toilet. Somehow we find it hard to believe that TV favourites like *Jeremy Paxman*, *Graham Norton* and *Joe Swash*, both urinate and defecate, and wipe their bottoms with toilet roll.

But like it or not, lavatories are as much a part of TV life as make-up and microphones. And one man who knows that only too well is Frank Crompton, who for the last 42 years has been a lavatory attendant at the BBC television Centre in London.

rolls

Over the years, Frank has seen it all. And now, after being sacked in a storm of controversy over missing toilet rolls, he has decided to spill the beans on the stars who use the lavatory, and make public for the first time ever their filthy and disgusting habits.

baps

"On screen, the stars look a million dollars. But most of it is make-up and clever camera angles. When you see them with their pants round their ankles like I have, their faces screwed up in agony, and you hear the groan of relief as their stools plop into the water, there's nothing glamorous about them, I can tell you.

jugs

The stars are well, known for their extravagant behaviour. They eat well, they drink well and they party a lot, and when they have a turd - boy! Do they have one.

melons

I'll never forget one log in particular (mainly because it wouldn't flush away, and I had to break its back with a lavatory brush.) Anyway, this one was laid by a particularly well known star. I'll just call her Judith, as I doubt she'd appreciate me giving her full name . But I'll tell you what, there was nothing Charming about what she left in my toilet. It had curled itself round the bowl three times, and stank to high heaven. I felt like sending her a postcard saying 'Wish You Weren't Here.' The smell was so bad that we had

Judith Chalmers: Three times round the bowl.

to close down the studio next door, and the following day the paint was peeling off the walls and ceiling.

soup

Funnily enough, it's the ladies who are worse than the fellas. What don't the birds chuck down the toilet, that's what I want to know. If I had a quid for every time I've had to stick my arm round the u-bend, in it up to my shoulder, just to pull out a clump of soggy tampons, I'd have a tenner by now. Probably.

garlic bread

One day the Director General rang me. He said that someone had been flushing fag ends down the pan, and they'd caused a blockage somewhere in the pipes. As a result, there was piss dripping through the roof of the Blue Peter studio.

Cilla: Ciggies in the loo.

Famous faeces: Frank Crompton spent more than four decades working behind the scenes at BBC Television Centre dealing with the stars' excreta.

That afternoon, I saw smoke coming over the top of one of the cubicles, so I grabbed a fire extinguisher and kicked the door in. Surprise, surprise! There was the late Cilla Black having a crafty cup of tea and a fag. I stopped her just as she was about to throw the fag end down the toilet.

ciggie

"I'll have that," I said to her. It had a bit of a duck's arse on it, but she was a good lass, Cilla, and she'd always give you a drag on her ciggie. When I explained

about all the problems she was causing with her dog ends down the pot, she was really embarrassed and promised not to flush them again.

booze

Another bird I recall for less pleasant reasons is Angela Rippon. Boy, was I glad when she left the BBC. Every time I saw her coming I'd say "And now for the Nine O'Clock Poos!" You see, she was terrible with her nerves, and every evening at about five to nine she'd come bursting down the corridor, farting like a tractor.

Angela Rippon: Pebble dashed.

It would be ungentlemanl of me to go into any furthe detail, suffice to say that whe she'd finished, it looked lik someone had been in and pebbledashed half of the bloody cubicle. And it tool some getting off, it did, let m tell you. I usually had to get hosepipe and jet the whole place down with water.

STARS' COCKS

e home about, I can tell you!

WORLD EXCLUSIVE!

There were one or two xtremely well-behaved stars ʼho would always leave the ·lace as they had found it. ʼhe magician Ali Bongo was ·ne, but how he did it, I'll ·ever know.

quick

One day he popped in ·or a quick dump during ·ehearsals for his show. I ·new it was him because I ·ooked under the cubicle ·loor and recognised his ·urly slippers. Anyway, he ·nust have had a massive turd ·ecause I heard the sound it ·nade when it hit the water. ·Ay first thought was "I hope ·he flush shifts that bastard, ·ecause I don't fancy going ·t it with a brush."

spencer

Next thing I knew, Bongo ·ot up and left - no wiping, no ·lushing. There was no sound ·t all. I thought, "Here we go, ·nother mess for yours truly to ·lean up." But when I got into ·he cubicle, I couldn't believe ·ny eyes. It was as clean as a ·vhistle. Nothing in the pan and ·o mess whatsoever.

engels

This happened on several ·ccasions. Each time he'd ·ay a log then leave without ·lushing it. But there was never ·nything in the toilet. So the ·ext time he came in I peeped ·ver the top of the cubicle to ·ee what was going on.

gran

What I saw was the most ·amazing thing I've ever ·een happen in a toilet - and ·'ve seen a few, I can tell ·ou. There was Ali Bongo ·tanding sprinkling his ·nagic "woofle dust" over an ·normous glistening log that ·vas so big it was practically ·limbing out of the pan. ʼhen suddenly…POOF! ·t disappeared in a puff of ·smoke. To this day, I've never ·vorked out how he did it.

Little and Large (above) - Large (below) and Little (above). Jimmy Nail (below) - Large nose, little cock. And (inset, above, below, right) Little and Large's Large pulls a face.

Hygiene is very important, especially when you work in a lavatory. So I would wash my hands every day when I got home from work. But some of the stars who used my facilities didn't seem bothered.

noodles

I remember one occasion where we ran out of loo roll. It was coming up to lunch time and I knew a lot of stars would probably fancy a shit during their dinner break. So I popped out to the shop to get some paper.

ted

When I got back I was surprised to see a well known academic quiz show host, who shall remain nameless, leaving the cubicle. What he'd wiped his bottom with I'll never know. But put it this

way - his tie was looking a little dishevelled to say the least.

trooper

Anyway, he then proceeded to walk straight out without washing his hands. Five minutes later I saw him tucking into a 'starter for ten' in the BBC canteen… with his fingers.

Roy: Big heart.

Some big-hearted stars made working in the lavatory fun, and I always looked forward to a visit from the late, cheery, multi-talented, tap-dancing trumpet player Roy Castle. Music was in his blood and he'd always sing while he had a dump after filming Record Breakers.

nanny

"Defecation. Defecation. Defecation, that's what you need." Those were the words the cheeky presenter would sing, and it always made me chuckle. And he's sometimes finish off with a little tune on his trumpet. At least I think it was his trumpet.

nintendo

On one occasion, Roy must have produced a "Record Breaker" himself. He dashed out of the cubicle and told me not to flush it. A minute later he came rushing back in with Norris McWhirter and a tape measure.

furry animals

It might have been a big one, but I think the record must go to now-disgraced *It's a Knockout* presenter Stewart Hall. One day he produced a specimen which was a knockout, quite literally. One whiff of it and I was gone! When I eventually regained consciousness we called in his old pal Arthur Ellis with his Halifax Brewery dipstick to measure the displacement of the water.

unleaded

While number twos are always the most exciting, it's the everyday number ones which are a toilet attendant's bread and butter. Mopping up the piss was a never-ending task. Of course, as I cleaned the floor I couldn't help but get a glimpse of the stars' cocks. And just like the stars themselves, their cocks come in all shapes and sizes. A fine example being Little and Large.

injunction

One day they popped in for a piss during a break from recording their great comedy show. And when I looked over their shoulders, I got quite a surprise. I'll tell you what, the names are right - Little and Large - But with no disrespect to Eddie Large, I think someone got them the wrong way round.

mario kart

Thursday evenings at the BBC studio were always busy because I'd get the Top of the Pops crowd in. Come to think of it, I must be the envy of every bird in Britain, because there's not one pop star's cock that I haven't seen. Mind you, some of them you have to try pretty hard to see at all. Like 'Microscopic' Mick Hucknall out of Simply Red. Don't worry girls - if you haven't shagged him, you aren't missing much, I can tell you.

drug

Jimmy Nail is another star who doesn't live up to expectations. I don't think 'nail' was a particularly good choice of surname. Jimmy Half-inch Panel Pin would have been more appropriate, from what I saw.

telly

Of course, it's not only the stars who have tiny tackles. A lot of high-ups at the BBC, like former Director General Mark Thompson, were short of a few inches in that department. And I suspect that jealousy may have been partly to blame for my recent dismissal. They said I had stolen some toilet rolls. But I'd only borrowed them and I was planning to bring them back the following day.

system

I think the real reason I got the push was because of my dead big cock. Frankly, I don't think the egotistical stars or snobby bosses at the BBC could handle someone working in the toilet with a much bigger cock than them."

HI, TOM. YOU WANTED TO SEE ME

YES, ROGER... BAD NEWS, I'M AFRAID

THE PRODUCER OF 'POP IDOLS' DOESN'T WANT YOU TO SIT IN FOR SIMON COWELL ANYMORE

SHIT! DID HE SAY WHY?

WELL, HE FELT YOU WERE A BIT TOO AGGRESSIVE WITH THE CONTESTANTS, ROGER...

BUT HE FUCKING **TOLD** ME TO BE AGGRESSIVE, TOM... SHOW NO MERCY, HE SAID. GO OUT AND **ATTACK THEM!**

HE ME **VERB.** ROGE

FUCK

ER, YES. A BIT LIKE THAT I S'POSE. BUT YOU HAVE TO ASK YOURSELF, WHERE DID HE GO WRONG, EH?...

WELL, ER...

WHERE DID BIG BROTHER GO WRONG?

SEX, TOM... Y'SEE, THIS IS THE CLEVER BIT - I'M NOT GOING TO BE IN THERE ON MY TOD...

...NO!..

I'LL HAVE **JORDAN** AND **JODIE MARSH** WITH ME!

IMAGINE IT, A **MONTH** AND A **HALF** OF LIVE THREE-IN-A-BOX HARDCORE...

ROGER...

THE VIEWERS WILL **LAP IT UP**, TOM.

ROGER...

OKAY, IT MIGHT BE A BIT SAUCY FOR THE TERRESTR EVEN CHANNEL FIVE...

ROGER.

BUT THE SATELLITE BO WILL TAKE IT NO BOTHE

11.45 NEXT MORNING...

WHERE THE **HELL** IS HE?

ROGER MELLIE'S 3-IN-A BOX 45 DAYS ON JUST 2 BIRDS AND WATER

SORRY I'M LATE, TOM... HAD A BIT OF A LATE NIGHT W STUART HALL... HEY, I TOLD HIM ABOUT THIS AN' HE THIN IT'S A FUCKIN' BELTER OF AN ID

THIS WAY, O FAIR DAMSELS! HAA! HAA! HAA! HAAAAA

GIGGLE!

STUART HALL PRESENTS - 2 MONTHS IN A BOX WITH 10 TV-X GIRLS

GIGGLE! SQUEAL!

WITH ...ASEBALL ...AT ...EURS!

AH, WELL! IT'LL BE A RELIEF TO GET OUT OF THESE TROUSERS... THEY'RE KILLING ME TITS, TOM

ZIP!

ANYWAY... I'VE GOT BIGGER FISH TO FRY... I'VE HAD A **GREAT** IDEA FOR A SHOW

IMAGINE IT, TOM... **ME!**.. SUSPENDED ABOVE TOWER BRIDGE IN A PERSPEX BOX FOR 45 DAYS...

WHAT!?!... LIKE DAVID BLAINE, YOU MEAN?

WHO?

DAVID BLAINE, ROGER ...THE AMERICAN MAGICIAN WHO'S JUST SPENT 45 DAYS SUSPEN-DED ABOVE TOWER BRIDGE IN A PERSPEX BOX...

BLAINE BOX STUNT IS TV TURN OFF

...ER, JUST STOP AND ...INK FOR A MOMENT

...5 DAYS... 45 **DAYS!**

...'LL NOT LAST 45 ...NUTES WITHOUT ...RINK AND A FAG

ALREADY TAKEN CARE OF, TOM... YOU SEND UP A FEW CANS AND A CHINKIES WITH THE WINDOW CLEANER EVERY NIGHT WHEN ALL THE VIEWERS HAVE SHOT THEIR BOLTS AND GONE TO BED

I TELL YOU, IT'S A SURE FIRE WINNER. WE'LL BE ABLE TO RETIRE ON THIS ONE, TOM.

PUFF!

WELL I WILL, ANYWAY

IT'S ALL ARRANGED. SEE YOU AT TOWER BRIDGE TOMORROW MORNING AT 10.00 SHARP...

DON'T BE LATE, TOM

...OULDN'T GET JORDAN AND THE OTHER ONE... ...EY WANTED A GRAND EACH... BUT THESE TWO ...L DO. A PAIR OF TITS IS A PAIR OF TITS, EH, TOM?

GIGGLE!

SLAP!

...GHT! LET'S GET THIS SHOW ON THE ROAD

HERE'S THE HOIST NOW

CRANE-O-HIRE

RIGHT, DON'T FORGET SOME CIGGIES WHEN YOU SEND MY GRUB UP TONIGHT. SEE YOU IN SIX WEEKS, TOM

ER...CRANE FOR MR....HALL?

SAYS HALL, HERE!

ER... IT'S MELLIE

NO... IT'S MELLIE

OVER HERE! HA! HA! HA! HA!

...EEEE! HA! HA! HA! ...AAAA! HA! HA! HA! ...HA! HAAAAAAAAA!

...CKING **BASTARD!** ...AT'S THE LAST ...ME I GET PISSED ...TH **HIM**, TOM!

GIGGLE!

AH, WELL, NOT TO WORRY, TOM. GOOD JOB THERE'S **PLAN B**

WHAT'S THAT?

THE MOST EXCITING TELLY EVER, TOM... **ROGER MELLIE'S LIVE RUSSIAN ROULETTE!**

LATER THAT WEEK...

what... what... what were the... the.. ...viewing figures... like... Tom? groan

SHHH! ROGER...

BEEP.. BEEP.. BEEP.

JUST REST! DON'T TRY TO TALK

ROGER MELLIE THE MAN ON THE TELLY

AH, ROGER...GLAD YOU COULD...

LISTEN, TOM! I'VE HAD A GREAT IDEA FOR A SHOW... GET THIS...

...ROGER'S BIG BATH NIGHT WHAT DO YOU RECKON, TOM?

HMM...IT'S A GOOD TITLE. GO ON...

WELL, HAVE YOU EVER NOTICED THAT THERE'S LOADS OF FIT BIRDS ON THE TELLY WHO NEVER GET THEIR KITS OFF...

EH?

ER

SO WHAT WE DO IS WE BREAK INTO THEIR HOUSES...

...OKAY?

...THEN WE SET CAMERAS UP IN THE BATHROOM AND FILM THEM HAVING A SHOWER...GOOD, EH?

RIGHT...YOU DON'T THINK WE'D RUN INTO LEGAL PROBLEMS AT ALL, ROGER?...SECRETLY FILMING WOMEN IN THEIR BATHROOMS, HMM?

LEAVE THAT TO THE LAWYERS TO SORT OUT...LET 'EM EARN THEIR MONEY FOR A CHANGE

ROGER, YOU REALLY SHOULD GIVE VIEWERS CREDIT FOR BEING A BIT MORE SOPHIS-TICATED THAN THAT.

THIS IS SOPHISTICATED, TOM...

...I'M TALKING CLASS BIRDS HERE...NO FUCKING SLAGS... CHARLOTTE CHURCH... KATHERINE JENKINS...

...MYLEEN KLASS...THAT SORT.

ROGER...PEOPLE ARE INTERESTED IN REAL WOMEN THESE DAYS... NORMAL BODIES...

...WHICH, ACTUALLY, IS WHY I ASKED YOU TO COME ALONG...

HAVE YOU SEEN THE SHOW HOW TO LOOK GOOD NAKED?

NOT SEEN IT, TOM, BUT I'VE HEARD ABOUT IT...

...GOK WOTSISNAME ISN'T IT?..GOES AROUND GETTING BIRDS TO STRIP AN' THEN COPS A FEEL

NICE WORK IF YOU CAN GET IT...

WHAT ARE YOU TALKING ABOUT, ROGER?...HE'S GAY!

HE'S NOT GAY TOM...IT'S ALL A FUCKING ACT!

HE JUST PRETENDS HE'S A SHIRT LIFTER SO HE CAN FEEL 'EM UP

I'M NOT GETTING AT HIM, TOM. GOOD LUCK TO HIM, I SAY.

LOOK...ANYWAY, GOK'S HAD A NASTY ACCIDENT WHILST HOOVERING THE STAIRS IN A LOOSE FITTING DRESSING GOWN...

OOH!

...THEY WANT YOU TO DO THIS WEEK'S SHOW

GET IN! I'LL HAVE A SLICE OF THAT, TOM

WELL, I'LL SEE YOU AT THE STUDIO TOMORROW, ROGER...

...FILMING STARTS AT 10.00. SHARP! DON'T BE LATE.

11.00 NEXT DAY...

HE'S ALWAYS AN HOUR LATE, SO I TOLD HIM WE STARTED AT 10.00, HE'LL BE HERE ANY MINUTE. ARE WE GOOD TO GO?

ALL SET, TOM

12.00

SORRY I'M LATE, TOM...I THOUGHT YOU SAID WE STARTED AT 11.00

WHAT DO YOU RECKON?

ERM...

I'M FREE! I'M FREE!... OOH, SHUT THAT DOOR, TOM

ROGER...NO, PLEASE

LOOK, IN A MINUTE, WE'RE GOING TO BRING OUT THE SUBJECT OF TODAY'S SHOW, SALLY, FROM HULL

OKAY

SHE HAS PERSONAL IMAGE ISSUES. SO SHE COMES IN IN HER BRA AND PANTS, AND YOU RESTORE HER CONFIDENCE, ROGER

HOW DO I DO THAT, THEN, TOM?

WELL, YOU TELL HER THAT SHE'S BEAUTIFUL AND SHE SHOULD BE PROUD OF HER BUMPS AND CURVES...

...THEN YOU TELL HER HOW TO HIDE THEM...WEARING STRIPES, NOT HOOPS... THAT KIND OF THING.

GOTCHA, TOM... RIGHT...LET'S GO FOR A TAKE, EH?

PLACES, EVERYONE

ACTION!

HELLO AND WELCOME TO HOW TO LOOK GOOD NAKED. AND TODAY WE'RE GOING TO MEET SALLY FROM HULL. COME ON, SALLY.

...DON'T BE SHY, GIRL

ROGER MELLIE
THE MAN ON THE TELLY

ROGER IS STARRING IN A NEW SERIES – "MELLIE UNDERCOVER"

HI, TOM! HOW'S LAST NIGHTS AUDIENCE FIGURES?

GREAT! "BLOWING THE LID OFF BRITAIN'S BROTHELS" GOT **8 MILLION** VIEWERS!

VIEWING FIGURES

IF YOU HADN'T CUT THE BIT WHERE THE BIRD WITH BIG TITS BLEW **MY** LID OFF, YOU'D HAVE GOT 20 MILLION NO BOTHER

BUT, ROGER...

SLAP ON THE WRIST OFF THE I.B.A, TOM... SO WHAT?

SLAP **ON** THE **WRIST**!?...IT WAS TEN MINUTES OF **CLOSE-UP ORAL SEX**, ROGER!

I'D LIKE TO SEE **YOU** GET A LONG SHOT OF A BLOW JOB WITH THE CAMERA CONCEALED IN YOUR FUCKIN' BELT BUCKLE, TOM!

ANYWAY, IT WAS **20** MINUTES...I HAD TO CHANGE THE TAPE HALFWAY THROUGH.

WHAT'S THE SUBJECT **THIS** WEEK?

IT'S AN EXPOSÉ OF AN ILLEGAL DOGFIGHTING RING

THERE'S A MEETING TONIGHT IN A DESERTED BARN JUST OUTSIDE FULCHESTER...

WE WANT YOU TO PUT ON THIS DISGUISE, INFILTRATE AND SECRETLY FILM THE FIGHT.

EH!? COME ON...I'LL LOOK A RIGHT CUNT ON A STICK IN THIS GET-UP, TOM...

...I'VE GOT MY IMAGE TO THINK OF!

BUT, ROGER, YOU'LL BE DEALING WITH SOME NASTY PEOPLE. IF ANYONE RECOGNISES YOU, THE CONSEQUENCES DON'T BEAR THINKING ABOUT

ALRIGHT! ALRIGHT!

BUT DON'T WORRY, TOM. I KNOW WHAT I'M DOING

THAT NIGHT...

EVERYONE'S STARTING TO GATHER...

...I WONDER WHERE ROGER IS

♪DEE-DA, DA-DEE-DEE DA-DA-DAA!♪

Roger Mellie ALBION ROVER

SCREECH!

WHAT THE **BLOODY HELL**...!?

SORRY I'M LATE, TOM. I HAD TO STOP AT A GARAGE TO GET SOME PP3s FOR THE HIDDEN CAMERA...TOM..!?...

...TOM!?!

...WHERE ARE YOU, TOM!?

AH, THERE YOU ARE. RIGHT, I'VE GOT THE STUFF FOR THE FIGHT, TOM

STUFF!? **WHAT** STUFF?

ROGER! **WHAT THE HELL**...!?

TAKE IT FROM ME, TOM, WHEN YOU'VE SEEN ONE DOG FIGHT, YOU'VE SEEN **THE LOT**...

THIS LITTLE FUCKER SHOULD LIVEN THINGS UP A BIT. IT'LL MAKE **GREAT** TELLY, TOM

ROGER! THAT'S THE CRUELEST THING I EVER HEARD. YOU CAN'T FIGHT DOGS AGAINST WILD ANIMALS

DON'T WORRY, TOM. I SNAPPED ITS TEETH OUT WITH PLIERS. IT DOESN'T STAND A CHANCE.

LOOK, WE'RE TRYING TO **STOP** THIS KIND OF THING, ROGER, NOT TURN IT INTO ENTERTAINMENT

BUT, TOM

THEY'RE **VERMIN**. THEY SPREAD V.D. OR SOMETHING.

NEVER MIND, ROGER...THE FIGHT IS ABOUT TO START. GO IN AND START FILMING. ONCE YOU'VE GOT THE FOOTAGE, GIVE US THE SIGNAL. THERE'S FIVE VANS FULL OF POLICEMEN DOWN THE LANE

LEAVE IT TO ME, TOM

SHORTLY...

SNARL! GROWL! GRRR! JEER! JEER!

THE FIGHT'S WELL UNDER WAY, BUT THERE'S NO SIGNAL FROM ROGER...I HOPE HE'S OKAY

HALF AN HOUR LATER...

I DON'T LIKE THIS, SIR. I THINK I SHOULD SEND MY MEN IN....

SNARL! SNARL! GROWL! JEER! R-IP!

NO! WAIT!

ROGER'S A PRO. HE KNOWS HOW TO HANDLE THESE TRICKY SITUATIONS.

AN HOUR LATER...

OKAY, TOM! CRACKLE! READY WHEN YOU ARE

THAT'S IT!..

...THAT'S THE SIGNAL!

GO! GO! GO! GO! GO!

NEE-NAR! NEE-NAR! NEE-NAR!

THUMP!

ROGER....WHAT ON..?

OH, HI TOM! SORRY I DIDN'T CALL YOU SOONER, ONLY I HAD A FIVE-FIGHT ACCUMULATOR ON...I GOT HALF A GRAND FOR A 20 QUID STAKE. NOT BAD, EH?

FOR GOD'S SAKE, ROGER...WELL AT LEAST WE'VE GOT THE VIDEO EVIDENCE...

...LET'S GO AND EDIT THE FOOTAGE

OH, BOLLOCKS! I FORGOT TO TURN THE CAMERA ON

GASP!! I...I...CAN'T BELIEVE YOU, ROGER

KEEP YOUR KNICKERS ON, TOM. WE'LL DO ANOTHER TAKE!

ANOTHER TAKE!?... HOW!?

SO...

CAN I HAVE A DOZEN DOGS, LOVE!? EIGHT PIT BULLS, TWO BULLDOGS AND TWO ROTTIES...

OH, AND YOU HAVEN'T GOT A COUPLE OF COCKERELS, HAVE YOU?

DOGS HOME

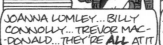

Welcome to the first annual *Viz* postal SUMMER

WELCOME one and all to Fulchester village green for the annual Viz Summer Postal Fete. And what smashing weather we have for it! Sunshine and fun are guaranteed all day long for this special fund-raising event, the proceeds of which will go towards Fulchester Parish Council's church steeple restoration fund. There's something for everyone. Fun and games, tea and cakes, competitions, exhibitions, prizes, raffles - there's even a display of dog handling by a local police constable.

In order to enhance your enjoyment of this Postal Summer Fete, why not try reading these pages in the garden whilst the sun is shining.

GRAND OPENING
by TV's Fuck a Duck presenter
ROGER MELLIE OBE

❝ *It makes me very proud, honoured, and two grand better off, to declare Fulchester's Summer Postal Fete OPEN.* ❞

OLD MRS THOMPSON'S WHITE ELEPHANT STALL

TAKE your pick from the various items of bric-a-brac on display. If anything takes your fancy, look up the price in the table below and send your money to Old Mrs Thompson's White Elephant Stall at the Summer fete address *(see end)*. Old Mrs Thompson reserves the right to send you a different piece of tat if the one you requested has been sold.

Books - 5p Records - 10p Nice painting - 35p
Table tennis net (some parts missing) - 5p Paint - 10p
Lampshade - 20p, Umbrella - 20p, Clock 15p
flowerpots - 5p (2 for 8p) Space gun (broken) 10p
Toilet freshener 6p, Computer stick 20p (electric)

GIANT FRUIT AND VEG COMPETITION

TO be judged by Mr Collins the Grocer. Do YOU have an unusually large fruit or vegetable? perhaps you've grown a big grapefruit, or cultivated a large carrot. Or maybe you've just bought a funny shaped potato or something. Send your entries to Mr Collins, who regrets that no fruits or vegetables can be returned. The winner will receive a rosette and a voucher worth £5 valid at Mr Collins' shop on Fulchester High Street.

DOG HANDLING DISPLAY BY

WOOF! WOOF!

R FETE

TOMBOLA

IT'S the luck of the draw in Dr Partridge's Grand Tombola. Tickets cost 20p (or £1 for a strip of 5) and you could win any of the prizes shown above. The star prize is a splendid bottle of QC sherry kindly donated by Fulchester Booze Buster store, High Street, Fulchester. Send your cash to Dr Partridge's Grand Tombola at the fete address and you'll receive your tickets by return. Check your numbers off against the numbers on the prizes, and in the unlikely event of them matching, simply return you winning ticket to Dr Partridge within 14 days. You prize will be sent to you by post.

MR AUTY'S WOBBLY WIRE RING-A-DING CHALLENGE

ROLL up, roll up! It's only 50p a go and it's all just for fun (no prizes). Can you draw a line from A to B without touching any of the lines? Why not have a go, then cut out your entry and send it, together with 50p to Mr Auty at the fete address.

BEER TENT   *SORRY! NO KIDS.*

WHY not sit down, relax, and enjoy a pint of warm, watery beer served in a cracked plastic glass. With a wasp in it. The following guest ales are all available from the fete address for the prices listed. In the event that your first choice is unavailable or the barrel is being changed, we reserve the right to send you the beer of our choice instead.

Fartwell's old Piss	£5
Barnfather's Titan	£5
Awld Bollocks	£5
Poldark's Old Original	£5
Foreskins' Forty Shilling Scrotum	£5
Merryweather's Apple, Nut and Woodchip Blunderbus	£5
Can of Ace lager	£5

REFRESHMENTS

EVERYONE is invited to bring along a selection of their own cakes for the refreshment stall. So why not send us a cake, and we'll send you someone else's cake in return. Then sit back and enjoy it with a nice cup of tea *(not included)*. Send your cake, wrapped in tin foil, please, to Mrs Alderson's Refreshment Stall at the fete address.

REK SCOTT & HIS DOG SHEBA

KIDDIES' GIANT BOUNCY CASTLE

WE regret that the bouncy castle has had to be cancelled as the verger's extension lead could not reach the compressor.

Send all your entries, cash etc. to the various stalls at the following address:
Fulchester Summer Postal Fete, The Village Green, Fulchester, c/o Viz Comic, P.O. Box 841, Whitley Bay, NE26 9EQ

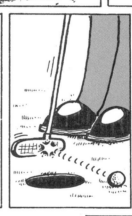

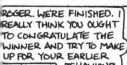

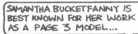

ROGER MELLIE

THE MAN ON THE TELLY

WHERE ARE THEY NOW?

● WHAT became of **TODD CARTY**, the Child actor who played Tucker Jerkins in the popular seventies children's series Grange Hill?

Heather Evans, Cardiff

● Well, Heather, Todd left Grange Hill in 1982 and gradually drifted out of acting. Nowadays, aged 86, he travels the country wearing a built-up shoe, earning a living from door-to-door, sharpening knives, grinding lawnmower blades and repairing pans and shovels.

"Grange Hill was wonderful work while it lasted," he told us. "I was earning a lot more than most kids of my age. But all good things must come to an end."

Todd has lost touch with the rest of Grange Hill's class of 1979, with one exception. "I knocked on a door a few years back and got a shock when Susan Tully opened it. She asked me in for a cup and we chatted about old times. Then I riveted a handle back onto a pan for her.

His job as a tinker may be a million miles from his acting days, but Todd insists he's never been happier. "I have no regrets at all. I'm my own boss now, and I enjoy every minute of it."

No regrets: Todd as Grange Hill's Tucker Jenkins (above) and below as he is today.

I USED to love watching the adventures of the young schoolboy spy **JOE 90**, but I often wonder what he did when he grew up.

Brampton Carlisle, Warwick Bridge

● Ironically, Joe 90 celebrated his 90th birthday yesterday with a quiet party at a retirement home in Filey, North Yorkshire.

Joe, who during the seventies starred in his own television show, has not been able to walk unassisted since his leg strings snapped in 1993. But staff at the Bay View Retirement Home say that he's in good spirits and was able to enjoy a glass of champagne to celebrate his birthday.

90 was declared bankrupt in 2003 after a series of failed business ventures. When his wife, Rhapsody Angel out of Captain Scarlett died in 2003 following a long battle with woodworm, Joe was forced to sell the giant food mixer in which he sat at the beginning of his TV show in order to pay for the funeral. The couple had no children.

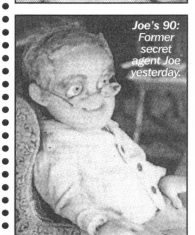

Joe's 90: Former secret agent Joe yesterday.

ROGER MELLIE

THE MAN ON THE TELLY

WED, 14TH DECEMBER...

HEY, TOM... GREAT IDEA FOR A SHOW...

NOT NOW, ROGER.

SORT OF A CROSS BETWEEN 'FOOD & DRINK' AND 'TOP GEAR'...

ROGER, I...

'STAR IN A REASONABLY PRICED BAR'. WE GET A LOAD OF DRINK-DRIVE CELEBS- JIM DAVISON, ALASDAIR STEWART, SHAKEY- THE USUAL SUSPECTS, AND WE STICK 'EM IN A BOOZER AND SEE HOW PISSED THEY CAN GET ON A HUNDRED QUID EACH...

LISTEN, ROGER...

...THEN AT CLOSING TIME, THEY JUMP INTO THEIR CARS AND THE FIRST ONE BACK TO BROADCASTING HOUSE WINS

WHAT DO YOU THINK, EH, TOM?

SORRY, ROGER... NO TIME TO TALK. I'M GOING TO A WEDDING AND I'M ALREADY RUNNING A BIT LATE...

A WEDDING?... ANBODY I KNOW?

WELL, YOU KNOW THEM, ROGER, BUT NOT PERSONALLY... ELTON JOHN AND DAVID FURNISH

IS THAT TODAY?

JESUS!.. I'VE GOT NO BIB AND TUCKER, TOM. WILL I BE ALRIGHT TO GO LIKE THIS?

WELL HAVE YOU BEEN INVITED?

NOT EXACTLY, TOM

BUT YOUR INVITE MUST BE FOR 2

YES...IT'S FOR ME AND MY WIFE...CELIA AND I ARE OLD FRIENDS OF ELTON'S

EH?.. HOW?

WELL, I DIRECTED ONE OF HIS VIDEOS BACK IN THE EIGHTIES.

WELL WHO ELSE IS GOING, TOM?

ER... LIZ HURLEY, MATT LUCAS, YOU KNOW...OUT OF LITTLE BRITAIN... ER... CHRIS EVANS...

...JUST TOO CLOSE FRIENDS.

EH!? WHAT THE FUCK'S THAT ALL ABOUT?...WHY DIDN'T HE INVITE ME?

MAYBE IT WAS SOMETHING TO DO WITH YOUR APPEARANCE ON 'ROOM 101'

...REMEMBER, ROGER?.. ONE OF YOUR PET HATES WAS "SHIT STABBERS"

ANYWAY, MUST DASH, ROGER. CAN'T KEEP THE BECKHAMS, ROD STEWART AND ROBBIE WILLIAMS WAITING

AAH! YES, I SEE, I SEE. IT'S ALL STARTING TO MAKE SENSE NOW, TOM... CLOSE FRIENDS MY ARSE...

ROGER... WHAT ARE YOU TALKING ABOUT?

I'M TALKING ABOUT HIM INVITING 700 CELEBS TO HIS WEDDING, AND THEN SELLING THE TELLY RIGHTS

AS IF HE HASN'T GOT ENOUGH CASH ALREADY... THE GREEDY LITTLE BASTARD

WELL THAT'S WHERE YOU'RE WRONG, ROGER. I KNOW FOR A FACT THAT ABC OFFERED ELTON SEVEN MILLION POUNDS FOR THE RIGHTS TO SCREEN THE WEDDING AND HE TURNED THEM DOWN FLAT!

SEVEN MILLION!?.. FUCK ME RAGGED.!!

YOUR TAXI'S HERE, TOM

GREAT!

GOT TO GO, ROGER...

WAIT, TOM, LISTEN... I'VE GOT AN IDEA. WHEN YOU'RE THERE, GET EVERYONE'S PHONE NUMBER, OKAY

EVERYONE'S, TOM. IT'S A SHIT-HOT IDEA

I'LL SEE WHAT I CAN DO

NEXT MORNING...

TOM! TOM!.. ARE YOU UP?

COME ON! WE'VE GOT A LOT TO DO!

JESUS CHRIST, ROGER! IT'S SIX O'CLOCK IN THE BLOODY MORNING

I'LL COME DOWN...

DID YOU GET THEM, TOM?

KEEP IT DOWN, ROGER

...GET WHAT?

THE CELEBS' NUMBERS

LOOK... I GOT A FEW... AS MANY AS I COULD... IT WAS VERY EMBARRASSING

GREAT. LET'S GET STARTED

ROGER MELLIE

BOLLOCKS

THE MAN ON THE TELLY

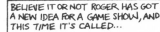

BELIEVE IT OR NOT ROGER HAS GOT A NEW IDEA FOR A GAME SHOW, AND THIS TIME IT'S CALLED...

MARBLES UP THEIR ARSEHOLES!

MMMMM. IT SOUNDS ABSOLUTELY MARVELLOUS ROGER

WE GET A FEW PUNTERS TO DRESS UP AS THEIR FAVOURITE SINGERS

THEN, WHILE THEY'RE SINGING, LESLIE CROWTHER STARTS SHOVING MARBLES UP THEIR ARSES!

AT THE END OF THE SHOW WHOEVER'S GOT THE MOST LIGGIES UP THEIR RING-PIECE WINS A FONDU SET

WHAT DO YOU RECKON TOM?

ROGER, I'D LIKE YOU TO MEET DIGBY RIGBY. HE'S THE PRODUCER OF 'ANY QUESTIONS TIME', F.T.V.'S LIVE BROADCAST SERIOUS POLITICAL DEBATE SHOW

HELLO ROGER. LOVELY TO MEET YOU

AS YOU KNOW THERE'S AN ELECTION TOMORROW, SO WE HAVE A VERY IMPORTANT SHOW TONIGHT. UNFORTUNATELY OUR REGULAR HOST, PETER SCISSORS, HAS EXPLODED, SO WE NEED YOU TO PRESENT THE PROGRAMME.

HAVE YOU DONE ANY POLITICAL DEBATE SHOWS BEFORE ROGER?

LET'S SEE... I DID A PILOT FOR 'IT'S A COCK OUT!' WE HAD AN M.P. ON THAT. ALAN ANUS I THINK IT WAS.

FUCKING GOOD SHOW ACTUALLY. DID THAT ONE EVER GET BROADCAST TOM?

NO ROGER. THE TAPE WAS SEIZED BY THE POLICE. WE'RE UP IN COURT ON TUESDAY, REMEMBER?

ANYWAY, WHY DON'T YOU STOP TRYING TO BE TOPICAL AND JUST SAY "BOLLOCKS"

THAT EVENING...

ANY QUESTIONS TIME

HELLO, GOOD EVENING AND WELCOME TO ANY QUESTIONS TIME

TONIGHT I AM JOINED ON MY LEFT BY CONSERVATIVE M.P. FOR FULCHESTER SUNNYOAK SIR ANTHONY REGENTS-PARK

ALRIGHT THERE TONY? BEST OF LUCK TOMORROW MATE!

THANKYOU ROGER

OVER THERE NEXT TO HIM WE'VE GOT SIR JOHN HARTLEYS-JAM, A "LEADING INDUSTRIALIST"

BIT OF A SMART ARSE OUR JOHN, HE SPENDS ALL HIS TIME TELLING PEOPLE HOW TO RUN THEIR BUSINESS, OR SOMETHING LIKE THAT...

I'VE SEEN HIM ON THE TELLY ANYWAY. THEN OVER HERE WE'VE GOT PADDY ASHTRAY...

...LEADER OF THE DEMOCRATIC LIBERALS

I THINK HE'S THE ONE WHO WAS SHAGGING HIS SECRETARY

WE'LL ASK HIM ABOUT THAT LATER EH!

AND OVER IN THE RED CORNER WE'VE GOT LOONY LEFTY SIR ANTHONY WEDGWOOD-TEAPOT

PERSONALLY I THINK PEOPLE LIKE HIM SHOULD GO AND LIVE IN RUSSIA IF THEY THINK COMMUNISM'S SO BLOODY MARVELOUS, BUT ANYWAY.

OUR FIRST QUESTION IS FROM A... WILFRED RICHARDSON.... WHO IS... TSCHHH! ....A "SOCIAL WORKER"

THANKYOU WOGER. DOES THE PANEL AGREE THAT THE WICH SHOULD BE TAXED AT 95% AND THE MONEY WAISED SPENT ON NEW HOSPITALS

'COURSE THEY FUCKING DON'T Y'DAFT CUNT! NEXT QUESTION

BLOKE WITH THE WIG... YEAH YOU... NEXT TO THE BIRD WITH THE SILLY TEETH

ERM... YEAH. DO THE PANEL FINK THAT THE ONLY WAY TO GET THIS COUNTRY BACK ON IT'S FEET IS TO CUT STATE BENEFITS FOR THE SCROUNGERS. THE TROUBLE WIFF THEESE PEOPLE IS THEY DON'T WANT TO WORK.

I PERSONALLY AM A TAXI DRIVER AND I FINK THAT IT'S ABOUT TIME THEY BROUGHT BACK HANGING.

MMM... A FEW GOOD POINTS THERE DON'T YOU RECKON SIR ANTHONY?

YES ROGER, AND IF I MAY I'D LIKE TO ANSWER THE QUESTION IN TWO WAYS. OBVIOUSLY THE GOVERNMENT ARE AWARE OF SHORTFALLS IN THE BENEFIT SYSTEM. OF COURSE WE ALL...

...SYMPATHISE WITH THE POOR, BUT I DON'T THINK GIVING THEM MONEY IS GOING TO SOLVE THEIR PROBLEMS. IT'S ALL WELL AND GOOD TONY TEAPOT TELLING US TO THROW MONEY AT EVERY PROBLEM THAT ARISES...

BUT WHAT TONY DOESN'T TELL US IS THAT WHEN LABOUR WERE IN POWER INFLATION, IN REAL TERMS, WAS.....

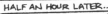

HALF AN HOUR LATER...

...FURTHERMORE, IF I MAY JUST FINISH... THEY COME OVER HERE, AND THEY TAKE ALL THE JOBS YOU KNOW. IT IS THE VIEW OF THIS GOVERNMENT THAT...

OH REALLY! THIS IS OUTRAGEOUS!

NO TONY... NO...PLEASE ALLOW ME TO ANSWER THE QUESTION... YOU'LL GET YOUR TURN IN A...

FUCKING HELL! THEY DON'T HALF GO ON A BIT, THESE TWO. I'M BORED SHITLESS!

HEY! EVERYONE SHUT UP FOR A MINUTE

FUCK THIS POLITICS! I'VE GOT A BETTER WAY OF SETTLING THESE ARGUMENTS!

SHORTLY... ANY QUESTIONS TIME

AND THE WINNER, WITH 27 MARBLES UP HIS ARSE, IS SIR ANTHONY REGENTS-PARK!

HOORAY! A VICTORY FOR COMMON SENSE

GOLF BALLS WOULD BE A MUCH FAIRER SYSTEM

RELAXING THE SPHINCTER IS ESSENTIAL TO INCREASE ONE'S ANAL CAPACITY

WELL THAT'S TYPICAL ISN'T IT. IT'S OBVIOUS THAT THE TORY WAS GIVEN SMALLER MARBLES

ONLY THIS WAY CAN CONSISTENT LONG TERM RECTAL GROWTH BE ACHIEVED

ROGER MELLIE THE MAN ON THE TELLY

GOOD EVENING TONIGHT ON **PANORAMA**, WE LOOK AT THE EFFECT A NEW BILLION DOLLAR OIL PIPELINE WILL HAVE ON **ECUADOR** - LATIN AMERICA'S FASTEST GROWING ECONOMY...

LOOKS LIKE I OWE YOU AN APOLOGY, TOM. I HAD DOUBTS ABOUT A LIGHTWEIGHT PRESENTER LIKE ROGER FRONTING A LIVE CURRENT AFFAIRS SHOW.

...ALSO DRAWN UP A FISCAL REFORM TO RECEIVE A SLICE OF REVENUES FROM THE OIL EXPORTED THROUGH THE PIPELINE...

WE WERE A LITTLE CONCERNED HE MIGHT DUMB IT DOWN, BUT HE'S HANDLING IT WELL.

... BUT BEFORE THE PROJECT CAN BRING ITS PROMISED BENEFITS IN THE SHAPE OF REDUCED INFLATION, ALONG WITH INCREASED PETROLEUM REVENUES, THE ECUADORIAN GOVERNMENT MUST SOLVE THE MASSIVE CIVIL ENGINEERING PROBLEMS IT FACES, NOT LEAST OF ALL, HOW DO YOU GET A PIPELINE CARRYING 6000 TONS OF OIL A DAY THROUGH THE ANDES MOUNTAINS?

WELL DONE, ROGER! I **KNEW** YOU HAD IT IN YOU!

...THE SOLUTION, LIKE MOST OF ITS KIND, IS REMARKABLY COMPLEX, BUT LET'S DEMONSTRATE...

...IMAGINE IF YOU WILL, THAT THIS YOUNG MODEL'S BREASTS ARE THE ANDES, AND THAT MY PENIS IS THE PROPOSED ECUADORIAN OIL PIPELINE...

GIGGLE!

ZZIP!

WHERE ARE THEY NOW?

I **OFTEN** wonder what became of the child actor **NICHOLAS BOND-OWEN**, better known as Tristram Fourmile, the boy next door in Thames TV's *George & Mildred* series.
Ian Wheelclamp, Swindon

● Well, Ian, Nicholas, who began playing Tristram at the age of seven, drifted out of the acting profession after *George & Mildred*. A millionaire at the age of ten, he invested most of his earnings from the series in a goldfish farm in Oxfordshire which failed in 1979 leaving him penniless.

"I enjoyed my time as Tristram," he said. "But I don't regret leaving acting as I wasn't very good at it."

"I've had offers to do pantomimes and the odd corporate video over the years, but I don't miss acting and I'm perfectly happy without it," he added.

Now 84, Nicholas owns a small printing business in his home town of Ashford, Middlesex, where he lives. He is married with 12 children, 32 grandchildren and 6 great grand children.

Caption: Tristram as telly viewers remember him (left) and below, Bond-owen as he is today.

★ ★

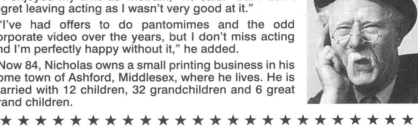

GROUNDBREAKING boy band **TAKE THAT!** were never out of the headlines in the 90s, and as a teenage girl I loved them. I once went to see them live at the Wembley Arena, but I was so excited that I wet myself and fainted and spent all the concert in the St John's Ambulance room. After their dramatic split-up they slipped from the public eye. Can you tell be what became of my heartthrobs?
Ada Trousers, Braintree

● Well, Ada, after their famous split, the boys took very different career paths in their life after Take That! *(Clockwise from the top)*

GARY BARLOW, the slightly bozz-eyed tubby one who penned the band's hits, was declared bankrupt in 1997 after blowing an estimated £40 on fizz bombs and sherbet dips. he now runs a small newsagents shop at Four lane Ends in Newcastle upon Tyne.

ROBBIE WILLIAMS, the first to leave the band bought a milk round in Ashby de la Zouch, Staffordshire.

On the band's break-up, **HOWARD DONALD** took the opportunity to realise a lifetime ambition and walk around the world. On his return, his dad got him a job at Boulby Potash mine in Cleveland, where he is presently deputy overman.

JASON ORANGE left the band with an estimated £10million which he invested in a revolutionary scientific process to extract gold from seawater. He now lives in a bus shelter in Peterborough.

MARK OWEN sank his money from the band into a gas-turbine powered mobile sex library specialising in under-the-counter farmyard pornography. Business has boomed and he now earns up to and in excess of £100 per week.

Postman Plod in...

diddly dum...diddly dee...

diddly dum...

diddly dee...

diddly dum...

diddly dee...

diddly dum... diddly dee...

This is the Night Train, crossing the border,
Bringing the cheque and the postal order,

All for delivery the following day,
Last post before Christmas, no time for delay.

Parcels from Grannies posted in Hull,
For grandsons in Aberdeen, Dunbar and Mull,

Wrapped in bright paper with colourful tags,
All must be sorted and put into bags.

Cards with their message of seasonal cheer,
"A Very Merry Christmas and a Happy New Year",

All posted with love from places afar,
Lying neglected, 'cos Plod's in the bar.

He's abandoned his post and he's having a ball,
Pissing his Christmas tips right up the wall, —

He's refined the consumption of booze to an art,
(A mile out of York he was pissed as a fart).

Ordering doubles and trebles galore,
Knocking them back and then shouting for more,

Shotgunning Special Brew straight from the tin,
His head's in a washing machine stuck on full spin.

Out of the buffet, through second class,
His guts full of lager, his arse full of gas,

He's got double vision, he can't feel his face,
His stomach is churning, he feels fucking ace.

Lurching like Frankenstein Postman Plod goes,
Elbowing passengers, treading on toes,

He trips in a doorway and falls in a heap,
On a soldier (gone AWOL for Christmas), asleep.

This sapper, of course, is a little bit pissed,
And woken from war dreams, he gets the red mist,

Using his skills honed on battlefield foes,
He headbutts the postie and knackers his nose.

This is the Night Train bringing the post,
For people to read over Cornflakes and toast,

Pulling up Beattock, a steady old climb,
The gradient's against her, but she's two hours late.

Spotting an empty seat, Postman Plod sits,
Alongside a woman with massive great tits,

Streams of saliva run out of his face,
He's rudely invading her personal space.

The lager fuelled Romeo fancies his luck,
"Smashin' tits, darlin'. Hic! Fancy a fuck?",

Her cries of alarm echo right through the carriage,
As she misunderstands his 'Proposal of Marriage'.

The Night Train
by W. H. Auden

These are the passengers, bound for their stations,
Off to their homes and their own celebrations,

This is the mother who's going to Fife,
To spend Christmas day with her son and his wife.

These are the children, off to see Grannie,
Cousin Matilda and Great Auntie Fanny,

This is the man with a big box of crackers,
This is the postman who's nursing his knackers.

In need of a tonic he heads for the bar,
Shuffling his way through the second class car,

Tripping on people, shouting rude words,
Passing the bogs that are blocked up with turds.

Sidling down corridors, catching his feet,
On people who've paid out good cash for a seat,

Back past the squaddie now covered in spew,
Then into the buffet, and front of the queue.

All of a sudden, along comes the driver,
Drunk as a bastard and waving a fiver,

"Can I push in, pal? I must get back quick,
Me dead man's-hic-handle's held down with a brick".

"Give me a tin of that lager, old son!"
"Ooh, you're in luck, mate. That's the last one"

"You cunt!" cries the Postie "gimme that 'ere",
But the driver retreats up the train with his beer.

Seeing his booze snatched from under his nose,
Chasing the driver, the drunken sod goes,

A kick to the arse and the driver is down,
As the train thunders onwards past village and town.

A kick in the ribs, a smack on the lip,
As Plod tries to wrestle the can from his grip,

A knee in the nuts, a knutt in the ear,
As Waverley buffers draw evermore near.

Locked into combat, the two drunken sods,
Are kicking each other in each other's pods,

As faster and faster, and faster and faster,
The train hurtles on towards certain disaster.

Plod leans on the door to recover his breath,
It's end of round one in this fight to the death,

But the latches are broke and he falls out the door,
(As has happened to hundreds of people before).

Here is the train pulling into the station,
Bearing the post for the whole Scottish nation,

Presents and parcels and cards by the score,
Still left unsorted in piles on the floor.

MERR...MERR CHRI...M...
MER...MER...HIC!...MERR...
CHR...CHRISM...HIC!...MER...
MER...CHRISM...HIC!.HIC!...
MERR...HIC!..

...AAAGH! FUGGIT!

ROGER MELLIE
THE MAN ON THE TELLY

The Sun — LIVER SWAP HOPE OF TV MELLIE

DRING-DRING!... DRING-DRING!

HELLO? ... TOM! IS THAT YOU?...

ROGER! OH, THANK GOD. I RANG THE HOSPITAL... THEY SAID YOUR OPERATION WENT WELL, BUT I'VE BEEN SO WORRIED.

EVERYTHING WENT FINE

THAT'S GREAT!

HOW ARE YOU FEELING, ROGER?

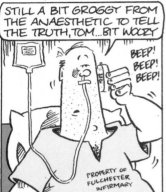

STILL A BIT GROGGY FROM THE ANAESTHETIC TO TELL THE TRUTH, TOM...BIT WOOZY

BEEP! BEEP! BEEP!

PROPERTY OF FULCHESTER INFIRMARY

WELL, I'M NOT SURPRISED, ROGER... YOU JUST HAD A LIVER TRANSPLANT

LISTEN, TOM...I...I NEED A BIT OF HELP

WHAT IS IT, ROGER?

WELL...THE TABLOIDS HAVE SENT SOME PHOTOGRAPHERS DOWN HERE TO GET SOME PICTURES OF ME, TOM

WHAT!?

THE ANIMALS! THOSE BASTARDS HAVE GOT NO MORALS! YOU'VE JUST HAD A MAJOR OPERATION!!!

MY GOD! JUST WHERE DO THESE PEOPLE GET OFF?.. TRYING TO TAKE PHOTOS OF A MAN IN HIS HOSPITAL BED!..JESUS!

BEEP! BEEP! BEEP!

HOSPITAL BED!?...

I'M NOT IN MY HOSPITAL BED, TOM

I'M IN THE KING'S ARMS OVER THE ROAD

WHA...

BEEP! BEEP! BEEP!

HOW ABOUT ONE HOLDING YOUR PINT UP, MR. MELLIE?

OVER HERE, MR. MELLIE...BIG SMILE THROUGH THE PAIN

GENTS

SPORT

ANYWAY, WHAT I WAS RINGING FOR...IT'S TURNING INTO A BIT OF A SCRUM DOWN HERE, TOM...

OVER HERE ROGER!

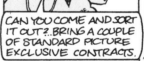

CAN YOU COME AND SORT IT OUT?.. BRING A COUPLE OF STANDARD PICTURE EXCLUSIVE CONTRACTS.

ONLY THIS IS FRONT PAGE STUFF, TOM... COULD BE A NICE LITTLE EARNER, THIS

THEY'VE GOT A COUPLE OF PAGE 3s COMING TO SIT ON MY LAP WHILE I DRINK A TOAST TO THE DONOR...

THEY'VE EVEN THOUGHT OF THE HEADLINE, TOM...

"THE LIVER BIRDS"

GOOD 'UN, THAT, ISN'T IT?

SLAM!

JESUS WEPT!

10 MINS LATER...

THAT'S IT, ROGER...GO CROSS-EYED AND LOOK ALL PISSED UP... THAT'S GREAT!

CLICK! CLICK! FLASH! CLICK! CLICK! CLICK!

SUN

NOW LOOK AT HER BOOBS AND PULL A 'PHWOAR' FACE

LOVELY, ROGER... PERFECT.. HOLD THAT

CLICK! CLICK! CLICK! FLASH!

SUN

PROPERTY OF FULCHESTER INFIRMARY

HOW ABOUT ONE STANDING SO WE CAN SEE YER ARSE THROUGH THE GOWN?

FLASH! CLICK! CLICK! CLICK! CLICK! FLASH!

OH, HI, TOM...BE WITH YOU IN A SECOND

FCUK

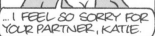

ROGER MELLIE
THE MAN ON THE TELLY

I'M TERRIBLY SORRY ABOUT THIS! ROGER IS USUALLY ERM... VERY PUNCTUAL... I... ER REALLY DON'T KNOW WHERE...

EEEK!

DA-DAAAA!

WHAT THE..!?

WHAT DO YOU RECKON, EH, TOM?

...THE BOLLOCK NAKED CHEF!

TITLE SEQUENCE... YOURS TRULY, IN THE BUFF, WHIZZING ROUND A MARKET ON A MOPED BUYING SOME VEG...

ERM...

BACK TO MY BACHELOR FLAT...

...INTRODUCE A GUEST COOK - A BIRD WHO'S STARKERS... AN' WE DO SOME RECIPES...

ROGER...

...WELL, SHE DOES, I'LL JUST WATCH.

DELIA SMITH SAID SHE'S INTERESTED, TOM, BUT FRANKLY, HER TITS ARE GOING TO BE HANGING IN THE MIXING BOWL

ROGER...

I'VE OFFERED NIGELLA LAWSON TWO HUNDRED QUID A SHOW, AND SHE SAID SHE'LL GET BACK TO ME

SHE'S A TOP BIRD, TOM. FINGERS CROSSED

ROGER...

THIS IS MARJORIE WATSON, SHE'S THE PRODUCER OF THE QUIZ SHOW 'THE WEAKEST LINK'

OH, HELLO, LOVE!

ERM...

YES... WELL ANNE ROBINSON, THE QUIZMISTRESS IS HAVING HER FACIAL HAIR WAXED. IT'S A BIG JOB AND SHE COULD BE OFF SCREEN FOR 3 OR 4 WEEKS

...IN THE MEANTIME, I WAS WONDERING IF...

NEXT DAY... HELLO AND WELCOME TO 'THE WEAKEST LINK'. LET'S GET STRAIGHT ON WITH THE SHOW... A BIG HAND FOR OUR FIRST CONTESTANT... PAUL FROM HULL

NOW THEN, PAUL... I BELIEVE YOU HAVE 3 GRANDCHILDREN. DO YOU HAVE ANY AMUSING...

CUT!

SORRY, ROGER. JUST A LITTLE POINT - ANNE GENERALLY PLAYS IT A LITTLE COOLER WITH THE CONTESTANTS... SHE DOESN'T GET FRIENDLY WITH THEM...

RIGHT

...LET'S GO AGAIN. REMEMBER... A BIT MORE STAND-OFFISH!

AND... ACTION!

HELLO. AND OUR FIRST CONTESTANT IS PAUL... ER... NO... ERM... MR. GREEN, WHO'S GOT 3 GRANDCHILDREN... ER... WHO WE'RE NOT INTERESTED IN...

...SORRY, MARJORIE... IT'S STILL NOT THERE, IS IT?

JUST REMEMBER... BE STRICT AND JUST A LITTLE UNFRIENDLY. YOU'RE THE NO-NON-SENSE QUIZMASTER.

RIGHT!

GOTCHA!

...AND ACTION!

RIGHT, YOU! GREEN! YOUR GRANDKIDS CAN FUCK RIGHT OFF... LITTLE CUNTS!

WHAT?

DON'T YOU FUCKING WHAT ME, YOU LITTLE WANKER...

COME ON! FANCY YER FUCKIN' CHANCES, EH? COME ON... STICK ONE ON ME

SHOVE!

C'MON, YOU CHICKEN SHIT WANKER! C'MON

NEXT DAY... I DON'T SEE HOW THEY COULD BLAME ME, TOM. THEY CLEARLY DIDN'T KNOW WHAT THEY WANTED

THEY DIDN'T WANT YOU TO BREAK SIX OF HIS RIBS, ROGER

IT WASN'T MY FAULT, TOM. ANYWAY, GETTING THE SACK IS LIKE WATER OFF A DUCK'S BACK TO A PRO LIKE ME.

WELL WHAT ARE YOU GOING TO DO NOW, ROGER? IT'S ANOTHER DOOR SLAMMED FIRMLY IN YOUR FACE.

OH, YOU KNOW ME, TOM. EVER THE OPTIMIST...

DRING! DRING!

SOMETHING'S BOUND TO TURN UP. HAVE I EVER LET YOU DOWN?

HELLO!... OH, HI!... YES... YES... OKAY...

OKAY, I'LL TELL HIM

IT'S NIGELLA LAWSON. SHE SAYS SHE'LL DO IT FOR TWO HUNDRED A SHOW, BUT SHE'S KEEPING HER KNICKERS ON...

...IF YOU WANT MUFF IT'S TWO HUNDRED AND FIFTY

BINGO! WHAT DID I TELL YOU, TOM?

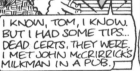

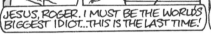

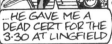

Roger's SHOWBIZ PROFANISAURUS

A Collection of Expletives, Crudities and Euphemisms from the world of Television, Media and Entertainment

amidships *euph*. A polite term used by cricket commentators, vicars and public school nurses to describe the *knackers* and *cock*. '*Ooh, Aggers! That delivery was pitched long, swung back in from middle and off and caught him squarely amidships.' 'Yes, Johnners. The poor cunt must be in fucking agony. More cake?*'

antiques scroteshow *n*. Any car-boot-sale-quality heirloom-valuation-based daytime television programme, *eg. Flog It!, Dickinson's Real Deal, Cash in the Attic etc.*

asboranto *n*. Grunt-based language used by those of low breeding when communicating with each other. '*What's happening on Jeremy Kyle?*' '*Search me. I don't speak asboranto.*'

barber of Savile *n*. A gents' hairdresser who typically purveys the sort of sex case coiffures favoured by *philanrapists*, trainspotters and 1970s showbusiness personalities.

Betty Both *n*. A *happy shopper*, a *switch hitter*. '*Yes, he is. I've heard he's a Betty Both and so is his wife.*' (Paul Lavers, unintentional live broadcast, Friendly TV, 2003).

Brucie bonus *n*. An act of *self pollution* achieved after summoning the image of saucy newsreader Fiona into the mind's eye. *Puddle jumpers* may substitute Radio 2's mid-morning hunk Ken, if necessary.

budgie supping *v*. The act of pitiful beer drinking performed by men who aren't used to it, *eg.* A terrified Tony Blair pecking at a pint for the benefit of TV cameras in Sedgefield Labour Club.

bullet-proof vest *1. n. milit.* Armoured clothing designed to minimise injury from incoming gunfire. Usually worn by news reporters trying to look butch in conflict zones. *2. n.* Reinforced clothing designed to minimise the impact of outgoing nipples. Usually worn by females in cold conditions.

cakeover *n*. That staple of the daytime telly schedules where they take a plain, fat lass, give her new clothes, make-up and hair, and she comes out at the end of the show looking like a plain, fat lass with new clothes, make-up and hair.

Cambridge Smith! *exclam*. A mildly amusing response to a *starter for ten*. Spoken urgently in the style of the excitable voiceover on BBC2 boffin quiz *University Challenge*. Also *there's no taste like Hovis; Congratulations, it's a boy*.

c and c *abbrev. Clips and cunts*. Generic term for any television programme consisting of nothing but clips from other televison shows/films/ads/videos interspersed with hilarious, insightful and profound comments from assorted *cunts* whose only reason for existing appears to be appearing on *c and c shows*.

cheeseboard Charlie *n*. Amusing pejorative term used to describe an individual who is excessively accustomed to big restaurant sessions. '*Oi, Cheeseboard Charlie, shut your fucking pie hole. Let Shirley Maclaine get a fucking word in edgeways, will you, you fat twat.*' (Michael Parkinson interviewing Peter Ustinov, BBC TV, 1978).

cock on the block, put your *phr*. Figure of speech comparable to "put your neck on the line". '*Earlier on today, apparently, a woman rang the BBC and said she heard there was a hurricane on the way. Well, if you're watching, I'm going to put my cock on the block and say don't worry, there isn't.*' (Michael Fish, weather forecast, October 15th 1987).

cockusoap *n*. A television serial drama, the cast of which contains a disproportionate amount of high quality *tussage, eg. Hollyoaks* but not *Last of the Summer Wine*.

council Sky *euph*. Free-to-air digital television.

cradock *1. n.* A *cock-a-fanny*. *2. n.* An old *cunt* with wonky, bright red lips. Named after the famous TV chef of the 1960s and 1970s, Fanny Cradock, who was an old *cunt* with wonky, bright red lips.

crinkles *n*. *Cock* wrinkles. '*Q: What's the first thing to come out of a man's penis when he gets an erection? A: The crinkles?*' (from The *Jim'll Fix It Joke Book*, BBC Publications 1975).

cuntourage *n*. The cohort of *twats* who accompany a radio DJ on his metropolitan peregrinations. '*Don't go in the bar, whatever you do. Chris Evans is in there with Aldo Zilli, Amanda Holden and the rest of his cuntourage.*'

debtors' dish *n*. Satellite television broadcast receiving apparatus. Term used by bailiffs and debt collectors who know that their indolent quarry will be at home watching advertisements for Wonga on the *idiot lantern*.

Dermot O'Leary's shirt, as wet as *sim*. Sopping. From the cuddly presenter's unfailing willingness to offer his shoulder as a tear-sponge to blubbing, over-emotional *X-Factor* hopefuls who've just had their dreams stamped into the dust by Simon Cowell.

Dickinson holiday *n*. A bottle of fake tan which makes the wearer look like a fucking satsuma. Named after bright orange cheeky ex-con TV auction wideboy David.

doley's blackout *n*. A mid-afternoon session of *self-abuse* snatched during a lull in daytime television. Achieved by shutting the curtains after *Quincy* for a quick *tug*.

double-yolked eggs, balls like *sim*. Of testicles, wrecked by over-exertion. '*Careful there, Precious. If you try to lift that fucker, you'll end up with balls like double-yolked eggs.*' (John Noakes, *Blue Peter*, 1970).

fart sucker *n*. A sycophantic *arse licker* or *shirt fly, eg.* Any member of Steve Wright's fucking "afternoon posse" on Radio 2 or fawning BBC News "royal correspondent" Nicholas Witchell.

FFFA *abbrev*. A reference to the sort of worthless *nonebrities* who rock up on the *shit pump* these days. Famous For Fuck All.

fifty-fifty, go *1. v*. On a popular television quiz programme, to have the computer "randomly" and unerringly remove the two less likely answers, leaving the contestant puzzling over the same pair of possibilities they originally suspected may have been correct. *2. v*. To risk releasing a *Bakewell tart* into one's trolleys, despite the fact that there is a very real possibility that it will be accompanied by half a cup of tea and a chocolate eclair.

floor chimes *n*. The collection of empty cans and bottles under the driver's seat of a regional television presenter's Jag, which roll together, producing a soothing jingle-jangle sound when the car goes round a corner, up a kerb or over a bicycle.

fruit & flowers *euph*. How drugs are referred to on television production accounting sheets.

fuck off moment *n*. During a person's morning commute, the point at which they decide enough is enough, mutter a foul-mouthed imprecation and switch off the radio. It is estimated that up to 80% of listeners to BBC Radio 4's *Today* programme experience a simultaneous *fuck off moment* at approximately 7.45am each day.

granny's flannel *euph*. An extremely dry *Cradock*. '*How did you get on fucking that bird last night, Russell?*' '*I did me best, Jonathan, but her cunt was like a granny's flannel and I couldn't get me cock in. Anyway, just before Sally Traffic with the travel news, it's time for the Radio 2 Record of the Week - On a Little Street in Singapore by everybody's favourite, Manhattan Transfer.*'

handy pandy *n*. A high risk *sherman*, taken over a particularly fetching children's TV presenter.

HRTV *abbrev*. Any daytime programme which is primarily aimed at bored, middle-aged housewives, *eg. This Morning, Loose Women, Des and Mel, Biker Buildoff etc.*

NEXT DAY...

'ERE. HAVEN'T I SEEN YOU ON THE TELLY?

John Sargent *1. n.* A *fry-up face*. Refers to anyone with features resembling the former BBC Chief Political Correspondent. *2. n.* A great British fried breakfast of which, before commencing, one might say "Now over to BBC Chief Political Correspondent John Sargent".

let's have a record *exclam.* A conversation-restarting phrase, to be deployed after a sudden *dropped gut* has silenced the room. To be delivered in the manner of Kirsty Young on Radio 4's *Desert Island Discs*, introducing the next tune after her guest has reminisced themselves to a standstill whilst re-living some childhood trauma or other.

Madeley's clipboard *n.* A flimsy defence put up in a vain attempt to hide a raging erection in the presence of, to pick an example entirely at random, a television studio full of swimwear models. Also *Parky's clipboard, Wossy's desk*.

mangerine *n.* A fellow with sunbed-roasted skin. *'Todays birthdays: Heather Mills, altruistic unidexter, 42; Melanie Jism, ex-Spice Girl, 36; Des O'Connor, television mangerine, 78.'*

masturmentary *n.* TV programme with a high *tit* and *fanny* count with a token bit of information thrown in to justify its showing, *eg.* A behind-the-scenes look at the pornographic film industry. The staple fare of late night satellite telly. Also *rudimentary, sockumentary*.

norks north *euph.* Tits up. 'Put simply, Huw, the fucking economy's gone norks north.' (Robert Peston, *BBC 6 O'Clock News*, every night for the last 7 years).

north face *1. n.* Brand name of a clothes manufacturer which seems suspiciously popular amongst BBC on-screen personnel. *2. n.* Mountain climber's euphemism for the more difficult route up a lady. *'Gladys had the painters in on the South Col, so Alf decided to attempt the tricky north face.'*

pensioner's tits, as low as a *sim.* Descriptive of something that is lower than one would reasonably expect. *'The ball pitched on middle and off and stayed as low as a pensioner's tits all the way to the stumps. A terrific delivery.'* (Bob Willis commentating on England v Zimbabwe, BBC Radio *Test Match Special*, Summer 2003).

poacher's pocket *1. n.* A fashion accessory favoured by illicit hunters and shoplifting celebrities. *2. n.* A very large *fanny* with a jar of coffee and some batteries stowed up it.

polar bear's arm *n.* A *fuck-off*, bumper-size line of *Bacon powder*, of the sort typically enjoyed in the *bogs* of fashionable London clubs by sweating chil-dren's television presenters. *'And here's a polar bear's arm I snorted earlier. Get down spiders!'*

Professor Pissflaps *n. prop.* An epithet given to a female who thinks she is more intelligent than the average bloke, *eg.* Any *bird* who turns up on Melvyn Bragg's *In Our Time*. *'Alright, Professor Pissflaps, you've had your say. Let some fucker else get a word in edgeways.'* (David Dimbleby to Germaine Greer, *BBC Question Time*, March 2002).

quim de la quim *n. Tussage* of the highest order. *'Well, that's the end of the evening dress section, and I think it's safe to say that the judges here at the Royal Albert Hall certainly have their work cut out tonight, because this year's contestants really are the quim de la quim. Now it's time for my favourite round, when we see them once again in their swimsuits, and I don't know about the viewers at home, but my cock's already got a bit of a twitch on and the girls haven't even come out yet.'* (Michael Aspel, presenting the *Miss World Show*, BBC1, 1974).

Rod Hull's aerial *euph. Brewer's droop*. Named in honour of the late Antipodean ornithologist whose roof-mounted **TV** reception apparatus proved to be somewhat less rigidly attached than he might have hoped.

satiscraptory *adj.* Decriptive of something of a poor, but adequate standard, *eg.* BBC local radio, the Edge's guitar playing, McDonald's food.

shitterati *n. coll.* Collective term for the heroic figures of the age who turn up on programmes such as *I'm a Celebrity, Get me Out of Here, Britain's Worst Celebrity Drivers' Pets from Hell, etc*. The kind of people who would happily fuck a pig if it were to get their face on TV, *eg.* Bubble off *Big Brother*, the coughing major off *Who Wants to be a Millionaire*, The Hamiltons, Katie Hopkins *etc*.

shit pump *n.* The television. *'I'm off to bed, love. Don't forget to turn the shit pump off when you come up.'*

smash it like a cheap glass, I'd *phr.* Humorous exclamation that signals a lecherous, overweight, impotent, sweating, purple-faced television football pundit's intention to engage in momentary coitus with an attractive young lady.

talk broken biscuits *v.* To speak in a somewhat unintelligible manner whilst *heavily refreshed*. *'BBC1, 11.35; This Week. The programme that brings you the big political stories of the last seven days. Join Andrew Neil, Michael Portillo and Diane Abbott as, fresh out of the BBC bar, they talk broken biscuits about the top topics in Westminster and the wider world.'*

Ted Rogers *n. prop.* A special sort of *gusset typing* utilising the lightning fast, dextrous finger technique made famous by the eponymous, late, fast-talking host of erstwhile purgatorial Yorkshire TV dustbin-based gameshow *3-2-1*.

TFFA *abbrev.* Initials never used as a catchphrase by erstwhile syrup-topped Radio 2 disc geriatric Jimmy Young. Thanks For Fuck All.

three dick gob *n.* A capacious mouth. *'The next record is You're So Vain by Carly Simon, the lady with the three dick gob. And it's for Terry, who is seven today. Lots of love from mummy, daddy, nana and grandpa Johnson and nana Robins.'* (Ed "Stewpot" Stewart, *Radio 1 Junior Choice*, 1974).

vin blank *n.* A missing period of time caused by over-indulgence in certain grape-based beverages. *'SUE LAWLEY: Keith Floyd, you're one of Britain's most popular television celebrities, but you weren't always in the public eye, were you? Tell me about some of the formative experiences of your early life. KEITH FLOYD: Well Sue, I clearly remember going into the pub on my thirteenth birthday and I vaguely recall getting out of a taxi outside Broadcasting House about twenty minutes ago. Everything between those two events is pretty much a vin blank, I'm afraid.'* (Transcript of *Desert Island Discs*, BBC Radio 4, broadcast on December 30th 1990).

zelebrity *n.* Somewhat oxymoronically, a Z-list celebrity. *'This Autumn on Living TV sees the return of Zelebrity Most Haunted Live. Some cunt off Hollyoaks, Becki from Big Brother 4 and the Duchess of York attempt to spend the night in a darkened room with Yvette Fielding, her fat mate and the bald bloke who looks like Uncle Fester.'* (from *TV Times*, August 2009).

ROGER MELLIE THE MAN ON THE TELLY

SO... QUIET ON SET...3...2...1... AND ACTION!

WELCOME TO GODBOX TV'S MISSION NIGHT, WHERE **WE** ARE GOING TO ASK **YOU** FOR £1 MILLION...

AMEN TO THAT, ALEX... HALLELUJAH!..**PRAISE** HIM!

AND WHAT BETTER TIME TO INTRODUCE MY CO-HOST... ROGER MELLIE

ROGER, WELCOME

GOD BLESS YOU, ALEX. HOW WONDERFUL IT IS TO BE HERE SURROUNDED BY GOD'S LOVE AND SPIRIT

AMEN...AND I THINK WE'VE GOT OUR FIRST CALLER OF THE EVENING...ADA FROM FULCHESTER...HELLO ADA... HOW MUCH ARE YOU GOING TO PLEDGE?

£10, ALEX

AH, GOD BLESS YOU, ADA...WE'RE ON OUR WAY TO THE MILLION... HALLELUJAH! ISN'T THAT GREAT, ROGER?

WELL, IT'S A **START** I SUPPOSE, BUT I THINK **GREAT** IS A BIT O.T.T.

COULDN'T SHE COUGH UP A BIT MORE THAN A TENNER?

OH, COME ON, ROGER...YOU KNOW THE STORY OF THE WIDOW'S MITE

NO!..WHO'S IT BY?

AND ON THE LINE NOW WE'VE GOT FRANK... HELLO FRANK... Y'KNOW, GOD TOLD ME YOU'D CALL TONIGHT TO PLEDGE SOME MONEY... ONLY HE WAS A BIT VAGUE ABOUT THE AMOUNT...

£15, ALEX

FIFTEEN POUNDS...

WELL, GOD ALSO TOLD ME THAT HE'S RESERVED A PLACE IN HEAVEN FOR YOU FRANK, HASN'T HE, ROGER?

WHAT? FOR FIFTEEN QUID? IT COSTS YOU TWENTY FOR A NIGHT IN A DSS B&B

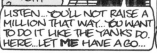

BUT FRANK HAS GIVEN WHAT HE COULD, ROGER. THAT'S THE IMPORTANT THING

IS IT **ARSE**!?..

LISTEN...YOU'LL NOT RAISE A MILLION THAT WAY...YOU WANT TO DO IT LIKE THE YANKS DO HERE...LET **ME** HAVE A GO...

BROTHERS...SISTERS...GODBOX TV NEEDS **YOUR** HELP TO SPREAD THE MESSAGE OF JESUS CHRIST TO THE WORLD...HE NEEDS ALL OF YOU TO CALL THE NUMBER ON YOUR SCREEN AND PLEDGE AS MUCH AS YOU CAN AFFORD...

...AND REMEMBER...GOD **KNOWS** HOW MUCH YOU CAN AFFORD

WHEN YOU OPEN YOUR BANK STATEMENTS, HE'S LOOKING OVER YOUR SHOULDER...

WHEN YOU PUT THAT CASH IN THE BISCUIT TIN UNDER THE BED HE'S WATCHING FROM INSIDE THE WARDROBE

AND IF HE THINKS YOU'RE **CHEATING** HIM, MAKE NO MISTAKE, HE'LL COME DOWN ON YOU LIKE A **TON OF FUCKING BRICKS**...

AND IT'S NOT JUST IN THIS LIFE, OH NO!..IT'S IN THE AFTERLIFE TOO...

BECAUSE GER-REAT WILL BE THE WRATH OF THE LOR-DER IF HE THINKS YOU ARE HOLDING OUT ON HIM...

...AND SWIFT WILL BE HIS VENGEANCE, AND MIGHTY WILL BE HIS VENGEANCE, AND HE SHALL FLAY YOUR SKIN, AND HE SHALL RUB SALT INTO THE SORES...

...AND SO SHALL YE BE CAST DOWN INTO THE FLAMING LAKE OF BOILING EXCREMENT FOR EVER AND EVER AND

EVER AND EVER AND EV...

ROGER, NO!..NO...THAT'S NOT HOW WE DO IT ON GODBOX TV... NO...

...WE WANT OUR VIEWERS TO GIVE THROUGH THE LOVE OF GOD...NOT FEAR

IT'S A BETTER WAY OF GETTING OUR MESSAGE OVER AND...

ALEX! ALEX! HAVE YOU SEEN THE TOTALISER?

YOU'VE RAISED A HUNDRED GRAND SINCE ROGER STARTED SPEAKING

R...REALLY?..A H-HUNDRED GRAND?

YES...THE PHONE LINES WENT COMPLETELY MENTAL...WHAT DO YOU WANT TO DO, ALEX?

2 HOURS LATER...

...IN THE BURNING PITS OF HELL-ER...BURNING FOR ALL ETERNITY-ER...WITH DEMONS-ER...POKING PINS INTO YOUR GENITALS-ER...

TELL IT LIKE IT IS, ROGER!

H-HELLO?..YES...A THOUSAND POUNDS... NO...NO...MAKE IT TWO...NO **THREE**!

HE KNOWS HOW MUCH YOU'VE GOT-ER! GOD KNOWS WHAT YOU'RE WORTH-ER. AND HE WANTS IT...

NOW!!

WHOOO!

A SPECIAL LEVEL OF HELL-ER AWAITS YOU SINNERS WHO DON'T...

ROGER! WE'VE REACHED THE MILLION!

EH?

GREAT!. RIGHT, THAT'S ME DONE THEN, TOM

SHORTLY...

HI, CANDY...WELL, WE'RE 50K RICHER... NOT BAD FOR TWO HOURS WORK, EH? SOON HAVE THAT SWIMMING POOL IN...DID YOU SEE THE SHOW, LOVE?

OH, YES, ROGER...

...YOU WERE MARVELLOUS...

YOU WERE SO GOOD THAT I CALLED IN AND DONATED YOUR £50,000 FEE.

W...W...W...

W...WHAT?...YOU DID WHAT?

WELL, I DIDN'T WANT TO GO TO **HELL**, ROGER

CHRIST ON A FUCKIN' BIKE

AH WELL, EASY GO, EASY COME...

...TOM?..HI... LISTEN...

...CAN YOU BOOK ME A STUDIO FOR NEXT WEEK

A WEEK LATER...

...AND GOD HAS TOLD ME THAT IF WE DON'T GET £50,000 TONIGHT FOR THAT SWIMMING POOL-ER AN ETERNITY IN HADES AWAITS EACH AND EVERY ON OF YOU-ER

...YES!..ONE THOUSAND POUNDS!

ROGER MELLIE
THE MAN ON THE TELLY

ROGER HAS BEEN CALLED INTO TOM'S OFFICE...

AH, ROGER...THANKS FOR... HEY, TOM. I'VE HAD A GREAT IDEA FOR A SHOW...

CELEBRITY PIG WANK! WE GET A LOAD OF CELEBS ON A FARM, AND THEY HAVE TO WANK OFF THE PIGS...

IT'S BEEN DONE, ROGER. THE FARM... CHANNEL 4

EH?...

HAS IT!?. FUCKING HELL!...I WAS ONLY JOKING AN' ALL, TOM.

JESUS..

...I'M GOINS TO HAVE TO UP MY GAME, I CAN SEE.

ANYWAY, WHAT DID YOU CALL ME IN FOR, TOM?

I'VE HAD THE SUN ON THE PHONE, ROGER

OH? WANT ME TO FRONT THEIR FUCKING BINGO AGAIN, I SUPPOSE

WELL, TELL 'EM TO **DOUBLE** WHAT THEY GAVE ME LAST TIME AND STICK A NOUGHT ON THE END FOR LUCK...

I WANT TWO PAGE 3 BIRDS SENT ROUND EVERY NIGHT AND A DOUBLE PAGE PLUG FOR MY AUTOBIOG, TOM... AND TELL 'EM WE CAN CHEW OVER THE DETAILS AT SPEARMINT RHINO **ON THEIR FUCKING TAB!**

NO, ROGER...

...THEY CALLED TO SAY THAT THEY'VE GOT SOME PHOTOS OF YOU.

PHOTOS?

YES...DOGGING, ROGER...

...IN THE LOCAL PARK. APPARENTLY THEY SHOW YOU HAVING SEX WITH A WOMAN ON THE BONNET OF YOUR CAR

EH?...

OH, THANK **CHRIST** FOR THAT, TOM.

PHEW! YOU HAD ME GOING FOR A SECOND THERE...I THOUGHT THEY'D DUG SOME **REAL** DIRT UP

YOU KNOW, I **THOUGHT** I SAW A FLASH GO OFF IN THE BUSHES

I WISH I'D HAVE KNOWN, TOM. I'D HAVE PROPPED A COPY OF MY BOOK UP AGAINST HER ARSE...IT WOULD HAVE BEEN A NICE BIT OF FREE PUBLICITY, THAT.

WHAT!?!...NO IT **WOULDN'T**, ROGER...

THERE'S A GANG OF MEN IN THE PICTURE WATCHING YOU AND **WANKING**...

THAT'S **NOT** GOOD PUBLICITY HOWEVER YOU LOOK AT IT.

BUT I'M A **MAN'S** MAN, TOM. EVERYONE KNOWS THAT. IT'LL DO MY REPUTATION THE WORLD OF GOOD

MAYBE IN THE PAST, ROGER. BUT AREN'T YOU FORGETTING SOMETHING?

DON'T KNOW TOM...AM I?

WELL, YOU PLAY A PARK KEEPER IN A SHOW FOR **TODDLERS**! IT'S THE MOST POPULAR PRE-SCHOOL SHOW SINCE THE TELETUBBIES

YOUR NEW SHOW ON CEEBEEBIES

UNCLE ROGER'S HAPPY PARK?..

WHAT ABOUT IT?

I CAN SEE THE HEADLINES NOW, ROGER...THE BEEB WON'T BE ABLE TO SACK YOU **QUICK ENOUGH** WHEN THOSE PHOTOS COME OUT

THAT JOB IS WORTH £250K A YEAR, ROGER. YOU CAN KISS **THAT** GOODBYE...PLUS ALL THE MERCHANDISE SPIN-OFFS THAT GO WITH IT...

FUCK!

...THE UNCLE ROGER ACTION FIGURES, THE HAPPY PARK DVDs, PENCIL CASES, JIGSAW PUZZLES, LUNCHBOXES...

FUCK!

...T-SHIRTS, PYJAMAS, SOCKS, BOARD GAME, INTERACTIVE CD...

YOU'RE ON 10% OF THE NET OF THAT LOT... WELL YOU WOULD HAVE BEEN.

FUCK!

THIS COULD FINISH YOU, ROGER. YOU'LL BE LUCKY TO GET THE ARSE END OF THE HORSE IN NEXT YEAR'S PANTO

FUCK!

WHAT AM I GOING TO DO?

YOU'LL HAVE TO PHONE THEM UP, ROGER...CUT SOME SORT OF DEAL

LEAVE IT TO ME, TOM

OKAY... JUST MAKE SURE THOSE PHOTOS NEVER SEE THE LIGHT OF DAY.

HELLO!? IS THAT THE SUN NEWS DESK?..

NEXT DAY...

AH, ROGER... I SEE YOU MANAGED TO SWING IT WITH THE SUN

SURE DID, TOM

...WE DID SOME STRAIGHT TALKING

THEY SAID THEY WOULDN'T REFER TO ME BY NAME AND THEY'D BLACK MY UGLY MUG OUT...

YES...THE ARTICLE REFERS TO "AN UN-NAMED TV PRESENTER"

EH!?. CHEEKY **BASTARDS**!...STAR WE AGREED ON...T.V. **STAR**!!

BASTARDS!

HEY, THEY DRIVE A FUCKING HARD BARGAIN, AN' ALL, TOM...

I'VE GOT TO BE THE FACE OF THEIR BINGO SCRATCHCARDS AND DO ALL THEIR TELLY ADVERTS THIS YEAR... ALL FOR FREE, TOM

FREE!..

...CAN YOU FUCKING BELIEVE IT?

NOT ONLY THAT, I'VE GOT TO WEAR A 'SUN' T-SHIRT WHENEVER I GO OUT THE HOUSE...

...AND I'VE GOT TO DRESS UP AS SANTA FUCKING CLAUS AT NEXT YEAR'S NEWS INTERNATIONAL CHRISTMAS PARTY

STILL, AS LONG AS THEY KEPT THEIR SIDE OF THE BARGAIN AND BLACKED MY FACE OUT, EH TOM?

OH, YES, ROGER...

THEY BLACKED IT OUT ALRIGHT. YOU'RE COMPLETELY UNRECOGNISABLE

...LOOK!

?

FUCKING **BOLLOCKS**!

'Having a Lovely Time'
PRESENTED BY
ROGER MELLIE
THE MAN ON THE TELLY

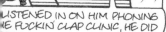

Roger's Telly Show WORDSEARCH

OVER the years, Roger Mellie has hosted hundreds of popular shows, one or two of which have even been given a second series. Hidden in the wordsearch grid are the names of 20 of his most famous. They may read horizontally, vertically or diagonally, backwards or forwards.

ROGER'S SUPERMARKET SWEEP - a game show with a shoplifting theme. **MARBLES UP THEIR ARSEHOLES** - an all-new game show requiring courage, skill and rectal volume. **CALL MY FUCKING BLUFF** - an old favourite with a modern twist. **THE ENEMA WITHIN** - celebrities share their colonic secrets. **THE GOLDEN SHOWER** - an adult themed version of the seventies classic The Golden Shot. **THE BRISTOL MAZE** - a breast-themed adventure game show. **THE BOLLOCK NAKED CHEF** - full frontal nude cookery. **ROGERING AROUND BRITAIN** - Roger tours the UK looking at the best brothels and rub 'n' tug shops. **PRO-CELEBRITY GOLF** - prostitutes and entertainers team up for a round of 18 holes, all for charity. **WHO'S THE DADDY** - Britain's first fertility clinic based game show **SPUNK IN THEIR EYES** - members of the public pay tribute to their favourite porn stars. **DIRTBOX JURY** - celebrities have the arses judged by a panel of experts. **BARGAIN CUNT** - two teams compete to see who can bag the best deals in Fulchester's red light district. **BRITAIN'S GOT DIARRHOEA** - stomach upset based game show. **THAT'S MY FUCKING DOG** - a show that combines illegal dog fighting with general knowledge. **ROGER'S BIG BREAK-IN** - Though the Keyhole inspired show featuring celebrities who are away on holiday. **CELEBRITY SHIT BUCKET** - D-list celebrities compete to see who has the best anal aim. **BIRDS OF THE RAZZLE HOUSE** - reality show featuring Roger Mellie and a dozen grumblemag models. **STAR IN A REASONABLY PRICED BAR** - drink driving based show where plastered celebs test their skills behind the wheel. **CELEBRITY PILL SWAP** - reality show looking at what happens when celebrities trade medication for two weeks.

```
A F D K R N I A T I R B D N U O R A G N I R E G O R B
K G T I L H T E X B J T G L P Z E O M Y L G V R S E L
R O G E R S B I G B R E A K I N D L H P N R E F E J I
M U G B S T M I B C S P E H Y G M U K D E M I L C S A
L R J K B F B M H K E C S A N L E S B C Z M I L H B F
Q U V H I G S O Z F V U E I S B U K G E A A B I K J E
S A C B K D U E X C Y E K M W E Z H O P M W N P L A G
T A R B E C H J P J W C A E N I O D G T L P M K Y E D
A D E I A M L D H U U Q H B I L F Y B W O M L A B T L
R L R R A X V I D F C R N Y R D L O W R T W B U W H G
I A Y D P U L B Y W C E Y A Z B U I O P S P P T D W X
N C T S W V Y M A V Y H J S T B O P H Y I P J E B H R
A R G O H T S P Y H M F R Y T Z E K E U R R P I L O V
R W B F H T E M I H D E T E N U L O I F B E B I D S C
E A N T A T L I M Y E R N U T Y G S E R E P G O A T E
A R T H E G O L D E N S H O W E R W T W H M T E W H F
S B T E E V F P J U F R M U E R D S V T E O B Y E M
O P Y R Q T E V F P U B M C D H U T M I A H P H H D C
N I M A G A S M U U O B T X T B E M P K R E A C O A E
A L F Z A U R E B U L E Z V I K A O L R W C D L J D L
B A L Z B U A P M F T B E G R R V R A P M E D C H D E
L A O L N Y R B U I J S G A S I R I G M K L M I Y Y B
Y Z G E E V I O L H M Y M N T C D L F A P M A V N T R
P T Y H P W E A V J L R S Y I T L E N E I E V I U E I
R E T O P L H E V U E O J Y O K V K M T E N P M V B T
I B I U M A T D Y P L H Y G A Y C L J G S E C P L G Y
C Z R S V Y P C U E B U S H I O V U P N V C U U C J S
E C B E A I U S P F R N V L M H I F P A E C T N B H
D V E I L D S D X Y I B T L N W C I T Y M I H Y D T I
B C L E J R E O F A L T O N I H T I W A M E N E E H T
A L E S E E L T I T F Y B C H T J B J L S C G L M Y B U B
R G C G N E B I C Y E C Y H N I S H Y F B U L N N K U
B T O A G I R O S H A V Y H D T V I K J E V E A M T C
R R M E B A C T N J G S B T E J I K N G R Y P D C B K
B U P Z R I M M T D S E Y E R I E H T N I K N U P S E
A Y H I P A W S L L I P Y T I R B E L E C A I Q G P T
```

EastEnder star's heartache

Street's Chris in fight for his girl

STAR'S CALL GIRL SHAME

Star's years of guilt haunted by gay secret

Tragic Street star finds a new love

Eldorado star Kai on the run

CELEB SQU

SHOPLIFTING SHAME

10

You are caught stealing a packet of biscuits from Sainsburys. You must throw *THE DICE OF SHAME*

9
YEW PERVERT

Your flat is searched by Operation Yewtree police. *Miss a turn* while you stand next to a solicitor and welcome the opportunity to clear your name.

8
HOSPITAL DRAMA

You suffer a heart attack. *Miss a turn*

CBB ARSEHOLE ALIENATES FANS

7

You take part in Celebrity Big Brother, but come over as a right cunt. *Miss a turn* while your career nosedives.

MY DRINK DRIVE SHAME

6

You are 'nick nicked' by police for drink driving. *Miss a turn.*

5
SOAP SUCCESS

You land a part in EastEnders and become a household name. *Move forward 10 squares.*

4
THE X FACTOR

You make it through to the final of a TV talent show. *Go straight to the top of the ladder of success.*

You have a drink problem and move to the Channel Islands where you pickle yourself half to death in a local pub. *Miss 6 turns* while you have fights with locals in the bar.

11

SOZZLED STAR DRINKS PINT OF PISS

Throw an **even** number and you are found 'not guilty' and get away with it.

Throw an **odd** number and you are convicted and overcome with shame. You must throw *THE DICE OF DILEMMA*

Throw between **1 and 5** - go back that many spaces. **Throw a 6** and it's all too much and you top yourself. *Take no further part in the game.*

MYSTERY ILLNESS

12

Mystery Illness. You check into hospital with mystery illness, and come out a week later looking ten years younger with a smaller nose and staples behind your ears. *Have another turn*

SEX AND DRUGS SHAME

13

You are caught dogging in a layby whilst ripped to the tits on crystal meth. *Miss a turn* whilst you explain to the press that you were innocently looking for badgers whilst ripped to the tits on crystal meth.

CAREER SLIDE

14

You finish second on the X-Factor final and are never heard of again. *Back to square one.*

An internet rumour surfaces and you are added to the list of celebrities who have apparently been stomach pumped after swallowing two pints of sperm. *Move forward 3 spaces.*

STAR TO HOST NEW DAYTIME GAMESHOW

PANTO DATE WITH LINDA LUSARDI

STAR 'DELIGHTED' TO JOIN SKY TV SHOPPING CHANNEL

LADDER OF SUCCESS

MY DEAF GRANNY WILL NEVER HEAR ME SING

Miss a turn while you reveal a source of secret heartache to *CHAT!* magazine.

2
CASTING COUCH

Miss 2 turns while a fat TV producer/PR agent has sex with you

SQUARE 1
Start

3

HERE'S your chance to be a Star for a Day. *Celebrity Squares* the great new board game that puts YOU in the shoes of the showbiz hopefuls as they struggle to ma it to the top of the ladder of success. Experience the thrill and spills, the ups and downs, they joy and heartache that are part and parcel of the roller-coaste ride of fame. Start square one and mo

60

HURRICANE TRAPS STARS IN PARADISE

HOUSE SLUMP HITS STAR

Cancer scare rocks TV Tony

BRAVE STAR WAITS FOR NEW LIVER

ng the board. The player to reach finish square has de it onto the A-list e rest are also-s.

ou need is a dice some buttons ct as markers. u haven't got buttons, you cut them off clothing - don't y, you can sew m back on again n you've finished ng.

19

NEW YEAR'S HONOUR ☆

Although you don't like to talk about it, except at every opportunity, you've done a great deal for charity. The Queen gives you a gong. *Move forward 3 squares.*

MYSTERY STAR'S DOG SEX PIC SHOCK

20

Builders steal personal photographs and sell them to the gutter press who hold them in their safe. *Miss 2 turns* whilst you appear in an advert for the Sun and waive your fee.

TWITTERSTORM!

21

A light-hearted tweet about the nazis is taken the wrong way and the twittersphere turns against you. *Miss a turn* whilst you wait 24 hours before everything returns back to normal.

22

'I'VE FOUND JESUS'

You discover religion and become an utter pain in the arse. *Miss 2 turns.*

18

☆

T.V. ad

Your agent has got you a job advertising stuff on TV. *Throw again* to see what you're flogging...

🎲 **Jaguar cars** - move forward 6 squares
🎲 **Nespresso coffee** - move forward 4 squares
🎲 **Walker's crisps** - move forward 2 squares
🎲 **Iceland Frozen foods** - remain where you are
🎲 **Pennine Double glazing** - go back 2 squares
🎲 **Quorn mince** - go back 4 squares

23

☆

SMACK!

☆

Your contract is cancelled after you punch a producer in the face. *Move forward one square* as you sign an even more lucrative contract with a rival broadcaster.

RN SHOCK

g pornographic pictures are entally leaked" from your and you hit the front pages. *ve another 2 turns.*

Affair 💘 Square

17

You have been caught having an extramarital affair and you take out a super injunction to protect your privacy. Miss a turn whilst your name immediately starts trending on twitter.

Odd number - Like Jimmy Carr, you are shamed into leaving the scheme and making an apology. *Miss a turn.*

Even number - Like Gary Barlow, a respectful silence is maintained and you get an OBE. *Have another turn.*

THE GUTTER | WEST END BROADWAY

TAX FRAUD

24

£ $ £ £ £ $ £

You embark on a perfectly legal, yet morally bankrupt tax avoidance scheme. *Roll again* to see if you are pilloried or left alone.

ONE WAY

25

'I'M BUST' SAYS STAR

You sink your money into *Save All Your Kisses For Me*, a West End musical based around the hit songs of Brotherhood of Man. Unfortunately, the show closes after three minutes and you lose all your money. *Go back along the Road to Ruin to square 1.*

IAC...GMOOH!

26

You hit the big time and fly to Australia to appear on *I'm a Celebrity*. *Throw again* to see what stomach turning delicacies you must eat in the Bush Tucker Trial.

ROAD-TO-RUIN

odd number - You're the only star death that day and are front page news. *Have another turn.*

even number - A Hollywood great has turned up their toes at the same time as you. You're on page 6 with the sudoku. *Go back 3 squares.*

R.I.P.

🎲 **Tarantulas' legs** - move forward three spaces
🎲 **Fish eye milkshake** - move forward two spaces
🎲 **Koala bear's nipsy** - move forward one space
🎲 **Emu's bellend** - move back one space
🎲 **Kangaroo's clockweights** - move back two spaces
🎲 **Iceland party platter** - move back three spaces

HACKED OFF!

27

A tabloid hack listened in to one of your answerphone messages 15 years ago, and the publishers offer you £150k not to press charges. *Roll the dice* to see if you put your principles before money.

Roll 1-6 - take the money
Roll over 6 - take them to court

FINISH ☆

TV STAR FACES FINAL CURTAIN

29

You are about to croak, and your death will make the front the front page of the papers providing nobody more famous than you dies the same day. Roll again to see if your demise is bumped onto the inside pages.

Question Time

28

Your decision to appear as the 'novelty guest' on BBC *Question Time* backfires as each of your stumbling attempts to address the issues reveals your staggering level of ignorance regarding current affairs. *Miss a turn.*

ROGER MELLIE
FTV

THE MAN ON THE TELLY

HI, TOM

ROGER...THERE YOU ARE!

GREAT NEWS... YOUR SHIP HAS COME IN AT LAST!

I'VE HAD NBC ON THIS MORNING FROM NEW YORK... THEY WANT TO BUY YOUR FORMAT FOR...

'ERE, TOM, TOM...

WHAT DO YOU THINK OF THIS?

PFFFFFT! PFFT! PFFT!

COUGH! COUGH!

JESUS!

COUGH!! WHAT IS IT? SOME KIND OF COUGH! FLY SPRAY?

NO, TOM...IT'S 'PRIAPIC' THE GREAT NEW SCENT FROM ROGER MELLIE

PRIAPIC

SCENT?.. COUGH!.. WHERE'S IT FROM?

MATE OF MINE... GOT A CONTRACT IN THE FAR EAST

COUGH!

SENDS IT OVER IN DRUMS LABELLED 'COOKING OIL'...SAVES ON THE TAX

THOUGHT I'D BEST EXPAND MY BRAND TENT, TOM... GET A NICE LITTLE INCOME GOING FOR WHEN I'M NO LONGER AT THE TOP OF MY TREE...

...DAVID BECKHAM, BRITNEY SPEARS... THEY'RE ALL AT IT

COSTS PENNIES TO MAKE, TOM. ALL THE INGREDIENTS ARE BY-PRODUCTS FROM AN ANTI-FREEZE FACTORY IN LAOS

HMM!

ANYWAY, THIS STUFF HITS THE SHOPS ON MONDAY, TOM. AND A 30 SECOND AD IN THE MIDDLE OF 'CORRIE' SHOULD SEE IT FLYING OFF THE SHELVES

CORONATION STREET?

YES! SO IT'S GOT TO BE A SHIT HOT AD...AND THAT'S WHERE YOU COME IN

ME?

THINK THAT TICK-TOCK TICK-TOCK GUINESS AD BOLLOCKS... BLACK AND WHITE... REAL CLASS.

PICTURE IT, TOM... A DESERTED BEACH... EARLY MORNING... I'M WALKING BAREFOOT THROUGH THE SURF... TUX OVER MY SHOULDER... FIVE O'CLOCK SHADOW

HMM!!

I'VE BEEN IN THE CASINO ALL NIGHT AND I'VE LOST THE LOT!... BUT I'M SMILING

...THERE'S A BIRD COMING TOWARDS ME, TOM... THINK SCARLET JOHANSSEN OR A YOUNG JENNY AGUTTER.... AS WE PASS, SHE GETS A WHIFF OF MY PRIAPIC...

...NEXT THING, WE'RE AT IT IN THE SURF... THINK 'HERE TO ETERNITY', TOM, BUT WITH BARE ARSES...

...WE GO OUT OF FOCUS. IN THE FOREGROUND IS A BOTTLE OF THE STUFF WITH A BIT OF SEAWEED ON IT...

YEAH!

A VOICE OVER SAYS 'ROGER MELLIE'S PRIAPIC'

DEEP, GRAVELLY VOICE.. THERE MUST BE SOME ACTOR AROUND WITH THROAT CANCER, TOM

YES.. NOT A BAD IDEA THAT, ROGER...SOUNDS UP MARKET, TROPICAL, CLASSY... I LIKE IT!

GREAT. WELL WE'RE SHOOTING IT TOMORROW ON THE BEACH AT REDCAR.

YOU BRING A CAMERA, I'LL TRY AND FIND A HALF DECENT BIT OF FLUFF IN THE PUB TONIGHT

NEXT MORNING...

JESUS, TOM. CAN WE GET ON WITH IT?...I'M FREEZING ME FUCKIN' NUTS OFF 'ERE

OKAY...

PLACES, EVERYBODY!

RIGHT, ROGER, YOU'VE JUST LOST A FORTUNE AT THE ROULETTE TABLE, OKAY...

YEP! LET'S SEE IF WE CAN NAIL THIS FUCKER IN ONE TAKE, TOM

OKAY ON SET...

3...2...1... ACTION!

THAT'S IT, ROGER... GOOD... RUEFUL SMILE

SPLISH! SPLASH!

GOOD... GOOD... LITTLE SHAKE OF THE HEAD..

THAT'S IT.. NOW YOU SEE THE GIRL APPROACHING

SPLASH!

...KIDDIES LIKE LITTLE BILLY, HERE...

...BILLY HAD NEVER BEEN TO THE SEASIDE, YOUR HONOUR...

UNTIL HE WAS TAKEN TO SKEGNESS ON A ROGER MELLIE FOUNDATION SUNSHINE COACH...

...KIDDIES LIKE LITTLE ORPHAN SALLY, HERE... SALLY HAD NEVER RECEIVED A CHRISTMAS PRESENT UNTIL THE ROGER MELLIE XMAS SMILE PROJECT GAVE HER A TEDDY BEAR...

...KIDDIES LIKE LITTLE TOMMY, WHO WAS GOING BLIND UNTIL HIS VISION WAS SAVED BY THE ROGER MELLIE SIGHT FOR SORE EYES FOUNDATION

THE LASER EQUIPMENT THAT RE-ATTACHED HIS LITTLE RETINAS WAS PAID FOR BY A CHARITY MARATHON RUN, DURING WHICH I SUFFERED A HEART ATTACK...

...YOUR HONOUR... IT WAS THE THOUGHT OF LITTLE TOMMY LIVING HIS LIFE IN DARKNESS THAT KEPT ME GOING TO THE FINISH LINE

...YES... IT IS **THESE** PEOPLE WHO I HAVE LET DOWN THE MOST... AND IT IS THESE WHO WILL SUFFER THE MOST IF I AM GIVEN A CUSTODIAL SENTENCE

SNIFF!

SHORTLY...

DID YOU **SEE** THE TITS ON THAT STENOGRAPHER, TOM?...NOT FUCKIN' BAD, EH?

FULCHESTER COURTS

JUSTICE

HERE YOU GO, KIDS... A TENNER A PIECE... NOW FUCK OFF BACK TO THE ARCADE

CHEERS, ROG

WELL, YOU DODGED A BULLET THERE, ROGER... FIFTY HOURS COMMUNITY SERVICE

HMM!

WE'LL GET THAT BLOKE FROM THE LOOKALIKE AGENCY TO DO IT... HE'S ONLY £2.50 AN HOUR

THAT WAS QUITE A SPEECH, ROGER. THERE WASN'T A DRY EYE IN THE HOUSE... IT WAS VERY IMPRESSIVE

IT SHOULD BE, TOM... I'VE GIVEN THE FUCKER OFTEN ENOUGH

GOT ME OFF MANY A DRINK-DRIVE BAN, THAT... **TWO** THIS CHRISTMAS ALONE

BEEP-IP! BEEP-IP!

OH, HANG ON... I'VE GOT A TEXT

WHO'S IT FROM THEN, TOM?

IT'S FROM THE BBC, ROGER...THEY WANT YOU TO REVIVE A CLASSIC DAYTIME T.V. SHOW

SEE, TOM... NO SUCH THING AS BAD PUBLICITY... WHICH SHOW IS IT?

OH, CHRIST!

A WEEK LATER...

3..2...1...AND CUE ROGER!

Roger's SUPERMARKET SWEEP

HELLO!...GOOD MORNING AND WELCOME TO ROGER'S SUPERMARKET SWEEP!

EXCUSE ME, SIR...

THE STARS WHO RE[...]

IN SHOWBUSINESS, as in the sky at night, for every star that rises, so another must fade away. Famous names and favourite entertainers for whom the show is over. Death, whether it be by accident, disease or natural causes, is no respecter of celebrity status. Eventually, it catches up with everyone.

But death does not always bring to a close the careers of the showbiz stars. For the entertainment world is littered with ghostly tales of stars who have simply refused to die.

KING'S RETURN TO THE THRONE

DURING his 46 years on earth, **ELVIS PRESLEY** never once visited Britain, except for one time. But an unemployed plumber from Altrincham claims to have come face to face with the King of Rock 'n' Roll in the lavatory of his council semi, *24 years after the star's death*.

59-year-old Bob Cartwright told us how he was awoken late one night by a groaning sound coming from his toilet. "I went to investigate, and couldn't believe what I saw," said Bob. "There, slumped across the lavatory seat, was Elvis Presley - the King of Rock 'n' Roll. He was extremely overweight and had been eating a slice of pizza. He had got stuck and was obviously in some pain." Then, suddenly, Elvis spoke.

echoed

"I'll never forget his voice. It seemed somehow distant, and echoed around the lavatory. But his Texas accent was unmistakeable," continued Bob. Elvis asked him for a spoon which he needed to take some drugs. Bob rushed downstairs to the kitchen, but as he ran back upstairs towards the bathroom door he heard a loud flushing noise, and turned the corner only to see bubbling water disappearing down the toilet.

u-bend

As the bowl refilled, Bob heard the unmistakable sound of Elvis's voice coming from beyond the u-bend. "He was singing *Suspicious Minds*. I'll never forget sitting there with my ear in the bowl listening as his watery voice gradually faded away. It made the hair on the back of my neck stand on end, I can tell you," he told us.

hamburger

Since that night, Bob believes that Elvis' ghost has returned to his house several times, on one occasion firing a gun at his television. "Fortunately, the ghostly bullet passed through the TV screen causing it no harm, but on another occasion Elvis caused a small fire in the kitchen when he left the grill on after cooking a hamburger late one night," he said. Fortunately, Bob was alerted by neighbours who spotted the flames and called the fire brigade.

Tree Terror Re~lived by dead Idol

DIESEL fitter Darren Peabody didn't believe in ghosts, until one night in 1986 when he had an experience he would never forget.

"I'd been to a friend's stag night at a local pub, and had been drinking heavily for several hours," he told us. "It was pouring with rain and I couldn't find my car keys, so I was delighted when a stranger in the car park offered me a lift home in his mini. In the light of the full moon, I made him out to be a young man, perhaps in his early 30s, with long, dark, curly hair and make-up."

hairpin

"I began to tremble as the car sped along the narrow, winding road. Thunder and lightning flashed as the car careered around hairpin bends. I asked the driver to slow down, but it was too late, for at that very moment the car skidded out of control and hurtled towards a tree. I covered my face and braced myself for the impact," said Darren.

urine

"The next thing I remember it was ten o'clock the next morning and I awoke to find myself lying in a pool of urine in the pub car park. There was vomit in my hair, and all over my clothes, and no sign of the young man in his mini. I made my way home and thought nothing more of the incident until a few weeks later when I mentioned wh[at] had happened to a friend. What [he] told me made my hair stand on en[d]. For less than 120 miles from th[e] very spot where the car span off t[he] road, pop idol **MARK BOLAN** ha[d] been killed in an almost identic[al] accident exactly 19 years earlie[r], almost to the month."

somersaulted

But the story doesn't end ther[e]. For six months later, after a hea[vy] night of drinking, Darren drove pa[st] the same spot and saw somethi[ng] moving behind the trees. "Throu[gh] the mist and fog I could just ma[ke] out the silhouette of a white swa[n] with someone riding on it," [he] told us. "Just like in the words [of] the T Rex song." Darren was [so] frightened that he lost control of [his] car, clipping a passing bus befo[re] somersaulting into a ditch.

hospital

"The next morning I awoke [in] hospital. I explained to the poli[ce] officers that I'd been frightened [by] the ghost of Marc Bolan, but th[ey] simply would not believe me," [he] said. Darren was fined £250 f[or] driving with excess alcohol a[nd] banned from driving for two year[s].

CAMPBELL'S PEA SOUPER

HOLIDAYMAKER Stuart Fergusson got more excitement than he bargained for the day he and his family hired a rowing boat for a day out on Lake Windemere in the Lake District.

snapped

Stuart, his wife Morag and their two children, Angus, 2 and Crawford, 5, had been rowing for about an hour when their oars snapped. Stuart takes up the story: "We were stuck in the middle of the lake with no land in sight. After a while it got dark, and a thick blanket of fog descended [on] the lake. It was eerie. Suddenly [the] ghostly calm was broken by a sou[nd] that made my hair stand on end."

speedboat

"It was the roar of a bright b[lue] rocket-powered speedboat. T[he] gleaming vessel emerged from [the] fog and pulled up alongside [us]. Without saying a word, the dri[ver] threw us a rope."

SE TO DIE!

THIS IS YOUR AFTERLIFE

INCE the death of **EAMONN ANDREWS**, dressing room number 66 at Thames Television has stood empty. For not one single star in the world of showbusiness dares use the room formerly occupied by the *This Is Your Life* presenter.

Andrews' successor, Michael spel, was the first man to enter the room after the Irishman's death. Seconds later, he fled screaming, his grey hair standing on end. It was several moments before Aspel had calmed down enough to describe his terrifying experience to horrified TV executives. For inside the dark, ngy dressing room, he had come ce to face with the headless ghost of his predecessor!

sprang

A Thames television insider explains: "Eamonn's ghost sprang at of the mirror and thrust a big d book at Michael. Fortunately spel fled, for the story goes that ayone who accepts the book from ndrews's ghost will immediately rn to stone." Indeed, one apless cleaner, while dusting the

lightbulbs which surround the mirror in dressing room number 666, was accosted by the ghoulish figure and took the book. She instantly turned to granite and her statue stands in the foyer of Thames TV as a warning to showbusiness celebrities and other would-be visitors to dressing room number 666.

Campbell's ghostly speedboat (above) emerges from the fog.

The next thing I knew we were ing towed back to the shore at eeds in excess of 600 mph, and it asn't long before we were safely ck on dry land."

explode

As I walked up the pier, I turned see the boat roar off at high eed, flip up into the air and plode in flames before sinking thout trace."

The next morning I returned to e if I could be of any help, but

there was no sign of the mystery stranger or his boat. Not a single bit of wreckage had been washed ashore."

fisherman

"I described the man to an old fisherman who was mending his nets at the nearby harbour, and asked if he knew him. 'Yes,' he said, 'That was the ghost of **DONALD CAMPBELL** who died 53 and a half years ago almost to the week on Coniston Water.'"

WHAT ARE GHOSTS?

THERE have been many attempts made to explain the phenomenon that we loosely term 'ghosts.' Are they simple illusions created by our brains, or perhaps figments of our vivid imaginations? Or maybe it's just our minds playing tricks on us. There have been many attempts made to explain this baffling phenomenon.

But what do the stars of showbusiness themselves think? Do the stars of stage and screen believe in the afterlife? And what is their idea of a ghost?

supernatural

We asked three former TV Dr Whos to offer their explanations.

White-haired former timelord Jon Pertwee has little time to ponder the mysteries of the supernatural. "I really haven't

given it a lot of thought," he told us yesterday. "But if you ring my agent next week, he'll sort something out for you," he said.

Suave time-traveller Peter Davison is in no doubt about ghosts. "The human eye is like a camera, if you will," he told us.

retina

"Images are taken in and focused on the retina. When you see a ghost, it is merely the same process happening in reverse, the image being projected through your eyes and onto the wall, like a slideshow, if you will," he added.

cornea

"I don't know anything about ghosts, and frankly I don't particularly care," recent doctor Sylvester McCoy told us. "And anyway, where did you get my number?"

Garden Haunted by Green-Fingered Ghoul

POLICE were puzzled when they were called to the *Blue Peter* garden at the BBC Television Centre. Vandals had dug up the plants, overturned a statue of the *Blue Peter* dog Petra and poured bleach into the Italian sunken pond.

Detectives were baffled. The gate had been locked, and the garden is surrounded by a six foot wall. "It's as if the vandals simply walked in through a solid wall," said a Scotland Yard spokesman.

paranormal

That officer may have been closer to the truth than he realised, for paranormal experts now believe that **PERCY THROWER**, the *Blue Peter* gardener and former TV bird impressionist, was responsible for the damage, and that his spirit had returned to earth to haunt the garden.

"Percy often spoke of his wish to be buried in the *Blue Peter* garden, alongside the box for the year 2000," one former presenter told us. But that wish was never granted. Show supremo Biddy Baxter refused to allow the burial, and even turned down a plea for Thrower's ashes to be scattered in the herbaceous border.

"Percy Thrower's spirit cannot rest until his remains are taken to the Blue Peter garden," we were told. "And until they are, Thrower's ghost will haunt the garden, vandalising it once or twice every year."

Next Week: The man who bought former Crackerjack funnyman Peter Glaze's house reveals how the star's spectre has repeatedly foiled attempts to decorate the building by the use of a supernatural bungling comedy wallpapering routine.

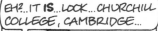

ROGER MELLIE
THE MAN ON THE TELLY

PHEEP! PHEEP! PHEEP!

WELL THE HALF-TIME WHISTLE GOES HERE AT FULCHESTER ROAD IN THIS FA CUP THIRD ROUND CLASH BETWEEN FULCHESTER UNITED AND PEDDLEWORTH ALBION... AND I HAVE TO SAY, WHAT A HALF IT WAS...

...THREE GOALS, A SENDING OFF, AND OF COURSE THAT RATHER CONTROVERSIAL OFFSIDE CALL FROM THE LINESMAN... OR SHOULD I SAY LINESWOMAN, TRISHA BRAHMS... A BIG DECISION... DID SHE GET IT RIGHT?

DON'T GO AWAY. WE'LL BE BACK WITH EXPERT ANALYSIS FROM JAMIE AND LEE, AND ALL THE SECOND HALF ACTION RIGHT AFTER THIS BREAK

AND... **CUT!!**

OKAY, BACK ON AIR IN THREE MINUTES, EVERYONE...

...THREE MINUTES!

WELL THE DAFT TART BALLSED THAT ONE UP, DIDN'T SHE, EH? A FUCKING **MILE** OFF, HE WAS. I HOPE SOMEBODY EXPLAINS THE RULES TO HER AT HALF-TIME

I THINK SHE GOT IT RIGHT, ROGER.

NO. NO, SHE COULDN'T HAVE

THEY SHOULDN'T HAVE BIRDS MAKING DECISIONS ON THE FOOTBALL FIELD... SIMPLE AS.

OH, COME ON, ROGER. IT'S 2011

NO... NO, THERE'S PLENTY OF OPPORTUNITIES FOR THEM IF THEY WANT TO GET INVOLVED IN THE GAME... **PLENTY!**

...THEY COULD WASH THE KIT... GIVE THE PLAYERS A PRE-MATCH MASSAGE... LET THEM ROAST 'EM IN A HOTEL AFTERWARDS.

ANYWAY, FORGET ABOUT HER DECISION... WHAT ABOUT HER TITS, EH? SHE'S GOT A CRACKING PAIR ON HER DON'T YOU THINK?

ER...

NO!? DIDN'T YOU SEE 'EM GO WHEN SHE WAS RUNNING, EH? **PHWOAR!** EH?... **I'D** SMASH IT, I TELL YOU... I WOULDN'T MIND HANGING OUT THE BACK OF IT.

EH?

HEY, LOVE. I THINK MY MICROPHONE HAS FALLEN DOWN MY TROUSERS. YOU WOULDN'T RUMMAGE AROUND TO SEE IF YOU CAN FIND IT, WOULD YOU?

...IT'S ONE OF THEM GREAT BIG LONG ONES WITH A ROUND END. HEH! HEH!

WHAT'S **HER** PROBLEM, THE FRIGID COW?... IT'S ONLY A BIT OF FUN...

...MUST BE A FUCKING CARPET MUNCHER. WHAT SHE NEEDS IS A BIG EIGHT INCH...

PLACES!

...BACK ON AIR IN 3...2...1...

ACTION!

WELCOME BACK TO FULCHESTER ROAD FOR WHAT IS SHAPING UP TO BE THE TIE OF THE THIRD ROUND...

NOW WHILE YOU WERE AWAY, WE WERE DISCUSS-ING TRISHA BRAHMS'S OFFSIDE CALL, AND THERE'S SOME DISAGREEMENT IN THE STUDIO...

...I THOUGHT SHE HAD A SMASHING PAIR OF JUGS, BUT JAMIE AND LEE WEREN'T TOO IMPRESSED

STILL, WE ALL AGREED THAT WE WOULDN'T MIND BENDING A LONG ONE INTO HER BOX, EH, LADS?

ANYWAY, ENOUGH OF THIS BANTER, LET'S GET BACK TO THE FOOTBALL BEFORE WE'RE ACCUSED OF BEING SEXIST.

JAMIE, WHY DO YOU THINK THE LINESWOMAN GOT THAT DECISION **SO** WRONG?

...WAS SHE UNSIGHTED BY SOMEONE IN THE PENALTY AREA, OR DO YOU THINK SHE MIGHT BE ON HER RAGS?

ROGER MELLIE

THE MAN ON THE TELLY

ROGER'S SOLICITOR'S OFFICE...

WHERE THE HELL'S ROGER? HE SHOULD HAVE BEEN HERE £600 AGO

AH, ROGER. THERE YOU ARE...

COME IN. SIT DOWN

MORNING, RONNIE

WHAT IS IT TODAY, RONNIE?... THE DRINK DRIVING, THE SHOP LIFTING OR THE SEXUAL HARRASSMENT?

NONE OF THE ABOVE, ROGER...

NO?

IT'S NOT THE DRUGS, IS IT? I THOUGHT YOU'D SORTED THAT ONE... GREASED A FEW PALMS

IT'S NOT THE DRUGS, IT'S NOT THE KERB CRAWLING AND IT'S NOT THE AIR-RAGE

GO ON, THEN. I GIVE UP!

IT'S YOUR DIVORCE, ROGER. I'VE HAD A LETTER FROM YOUR WIFE'S BRIEF

WHAT THE FUCK DOES SHE WANT **NOW**?

I SAID SHE COULD KEEP ALL HER CLOTHES... WHAT MORE CAN I DO

SHE WANTS HALF OF THE LOT

WHAT?

THE GREEDY BITCH. AFTER SHE'S DRAGGED MY NAME THROUGH THE FUCKIN' MUD

Y'CAN'T OPEN THE FUCKING PAPER WITHOUT READING SOME RUBBISH ABOUT HOW I SUPPOSEDLY HIT HER

YOU'RE SAYING SHE'S **LYING** ROGER?... THAT COULD HELP YOUR CASE

SHE ALLEGES HERE THAT YOU PUNCHED HER IN THE FACE... I MEAN... IS THAT **TRUE**, ROGER?

IS IT **BOLLOCKS**! I'VE NEVER PUNCHED HER IN THE FACE...

...I **SLAPPED** HER IN THE FACE...

...PUNCHED HER IN THE **STOMACH**...

...MIND YOU, I WAS PROVOKED, RONNIE

HMM! WELL SHE ALLEGES YOU HAVE CONSTANTLY ASSAULTED HER THROUGHOUT THE MARRIAGE

RUBBISH! I'M NOT A VIOLENT MAN, RONNIE...YOU ASK TOM

TOM...YOU'VE BEEN ROUND MY HOUSE WHEN I HAVEN'T HIT THE MISSUS, HAVEN'T YOU?

ERM...YES... A COUPLE OF TIMES

THERE YOU GO. CHARACTER WITNESS. HE'LL STAND UP AND SAY THAT IN COURT

NOW, HOLD ON, ROGER

LET'S TRY TO KEEP THIS OUT OF COURT IF WE CAN

NO, IT'LL BE FINE. THERE ARE LOADS OF JUDGES IN MY MASONIC LODGE... IT'LL BE JUST A MATTER OF TURNING UP, RONNIE.

HMM! I'M NOT SO SURE, ROGER...

IT WOULD LIKELY BE A JURY HEARING THE CASE...AND THEY'RE LIKELY TO SIDE WITH YOUR WIFE

NO, SURELY NOT, RONNIE. I'M ON THE BOX...A CELEB... I'M A HOUSEHOLD NAME

BUT SHE'S WINNING THE P.R. BATTLE HANDS DOWN... JUST LOOK AT TODAY'S SUN...

YEAH...

...BUT THAT'S JUST **ONE** PAPER

...AND THE MIRROR

TWO PAPERS, THEN

OKAY. SO I'M FACING AN UPHILL STRUGGLE TO WIN OVER THE PUBLIC'S HEARTS

LOOK. PERHAPS YOU SHOULD CUT YOUR LOSSES AND SETTLE OUT OF COURT, ROGER.

FUCK OFF!

I'M NOT BACKING DOWN, RONNIE, NO FUCKING WAY... WHEN THE GOING GETS TOUGH, THE TOUGH GET GOING...

IF SHE THINKS SHE'S GETTING ANOTHER PENNY FROM ME, SHE'S GOT ANOTHER THINK COMING

COME ON, TOM. WE'VE GOT WORK TO DO... GET ON THE BLOWER TO MAX CLIFFORD

TELL HIM ROGER MELLIE IS READY TO SPILL THE BEANS ON HIS MARRIAGE...

GET HIM TO SORT OUT A NICE LITTLE P.R. TOUR

NEXT MORNING...

SOB!..

...SOB! SOB!.. AND...AND ANOTHER TIME... I HAD TO... SNIFF!.. TO LOAD THE DISHWASHER... ALL BY MYSELF...

SNIFF! SOB!

OCH, POOR ROGER

...AND SHE REGULARLY SERVED MY DINNER FIVE, TEN... EVEN TWENTY MINUTES LATE...

SOB! SNIFF! BLUB!

...AND I'VE BEEN PAINTED THE VILLAIN OF THE PIECE...SOB!.. THE PRESS HAVE TRET ME WORSE THAN A PAEDOPHILE...

SOB!.. AN' ALL I'VE EVER DONE IS WORK FOR CHARITY FOR FORTY YEARS!..BLUB!

WAIL!

BOO!..HOO!..HOO!..HOO!..PRESS..MURDERER ...PAEDOPHILE... CHARITY..SOB!.. BLUB!

I THINK WE'D BETTER END IT THERE... ROGER IS IN NO STATE TO CONTINUE.

SOB!

ARE WE OFF!?.. RIGHT, WHERE TO NEXT, TOM?

ER.... 'PHIL & FERN', THEN 'DES K MEL', 'PAUL OGRADY', 'ADRIAN CHILES', AND THEN STEPHEN SACKUR ON 'HARDTALK'

OH! HAVE YOU GOT ANYTHING STRONGER THAN THESE ONIONS?

I WAS STRUGGLING A BIT TO TURN THE WATERWORKS ON THERE, TOM

HAVE YOU TRIED PUTTING A BIT OF VIC UNDER EACH EYE, ROGER?

THAT'S AN IDEA

WE HAD YOUR WIFE ON LAST WEEK AND THAT'S WHAT SHE DID... WORKED A TREAT.

ROGER MELLIE

THE MAN ON THE TELLY

1962...

WHERE THE HELL IS MELLIE? HE WAS SUPPOSED TO BE HERE FOR HIS CAREERS INTERVIEW 20 MINUTES AGO

SORRY I'M LATE, SIR

AH, MELLIE. GOOD OF YOU TO JOIN ME, BOY... HAVING A QUICK SMOKE BEHIND THE BIKE SHEDS I SHOULD-NT WONDER

NO, SIR...CERTAINLY NOT, SIR...

...I WAS IN A PISSING UP THE WALL CONTEST IN THE BOGS

LANGUAGE

NOW...DO YOU HAVE ANY IDEA WHAT YOU'D LIKE TO DO WHEN YOU LEAVE HERE?...A PLUMBER, PERHAPS? WE'LL ALWAYS NEED PLUMBERS

NO, SIR...

I'D LIKE TO WORK IN TELEVISION

TELEVISION!?..NO CHANCE BOY... NO CHANCE AT ALL... I MEAN, JUST LOOK AT YOUR LAST REPORT

ENGLISH-F... HISTORY-F... GEOGRAPHY-UNGRADED...

BOTTOM OF THE CLASS IN EVERY SUBJECT, MELLIE!

I MEAN... TELEVISION PERSONALITIES ARE INVITED INTO THE NATION'S FRONT ROOMS EACH EVENING...

...THEY MUST BE WELL PRESENTED, ARTICULATE, INFORMATIVE, INTELLIGENT... AND THERE HAS TO BE A GOOD REASON TO APPEAR ON THE TELEVISION, BOY... HE HAS TO HAVE SOME-THING TO OFFER...

...A SKILL OR TALENT

IN THE FUTURE, TELEVISION WILL BE THE MOST POWERFUL EDUCATIONAL TOOL IN THE WORLD... APPEARING ON IT WILL BE AN ENORMOUS RESPONSIBILITY...IT WILL TEACH... EDUCATE... INFORM...

IT WILL ENRICH THE LIFE OF THE VIEWER, MELLIE...IT WILL LEAVE THEM FEELING IMPROVED AND WISER IN EVERY WAY...

44 YEARS LATER...

WELCOME BACK TO 'CELEBRITY GENITAL MUTILATION'...

NOW, ROGER...YOU HAVE 30 SECONDS TO HAMMER AS MANY NAILS THROUGH YOUR FORESKIN AS POSSIBLE... 12 OR MORE AND YOU JOIN NEIL HAMILTON IN THE 'SCROTUM MANGLE ROUND'..READY?

READY...

NAIL IT ROGER

ROGER MELLIE THE MAN ON THE TELLY

MONDAY...

MORNING, TOM...HOW'S IT HANGING?

ROGER...YOU'RE AN **HOUR** LATE

OH, I DON'T THINK SO, TOM...

...LOOKS LIKE SOMEBODY FORGOT THE CLOCKS ALL CHANGED AT THE WEEKEND

WHAT!?...OH...YES...OF COURSE THEY DID...SORRY

...I'LL JUST PUT MY WATCH RIGHT....THERE!

ROGER, YOU'RE TWO HOURS LATE

YES, SORRY, TOM I OVERSLEPT. THEN I HAD TO STOP AT THE OFFY TO PICK UP MY BREAKFAST

I'VE HAD SOMEONE ON THE PHONE AFTER YOU THIS MORNING.

IF IT'S YEWTREE AGAIN, TELL 'EM TO FUCK OFF, TOM...I'M UNTOUCHABLE ME WITH ALL THAT CHARITY WORK

NO ROGER, IT WASN'T...

GLUG...GLUG.

THE COPPERS WOULD LOOK RIGHT CUNTS IF THEY HAULED ME IN FOR PINCHING SOME BIRD'S ARSE IN THE SEVENTIES

IT WASN'T THE POLICE, ROGER. IT WAS A JOB OFFER

I'M THEIR MAN, TOM. WHAT IS IT?

IT'S A LATE NIGHT ROULETTE SHOW

OH, I'VE SEEN THAT

IT COMES ON AFTER THE PROPER TELLY STOPS

SOME TWAT SPINS A WHEEL WHILE GAMBLING ADDICTED INSOMNIACS GAMBLE AWAY THEIR DOLE MONEY. WHAT DO THEY WANT **ME** FOR? I'M A **BROADCASTER**, NOT A FUCKIN' BOOKIES RUNNER

HAVE THEY TRIED PAUL ROSS?

WELL, THEY'RE TRYING TO ADD A BIT OF **GLAMOUR** TO THE PROCEEDINGS...THEY WANT TO EVOKE AN AIR OF LAS VEGAS SOPHISTICATION...HIGH ROLLER AT MONTE CARLO

HMM?

NEXT NIGHT...

SPINSPIN T.V.

EVENING, TOM. DO YOU LIKE THE SCHMUTTER?

ERM...YES, ROGER...VERY SMART...VERY CLASSY

SPINSPIN T.V.

SSTV

ROGER, WHEN ARE WE ON THE AIR? GIGGLE!

ABOUT FIVE MINUTES. HOLD YOUR HORSES.

CAN I SAY HELLO TO MY MOM?

ROGER!?...WHAT'S GOING ON?...WHO'S THAT GIRL?

ERM...HOLD ON, TOM

WHAT'S YOUR NAME AGAIN, LOVE?

SIMONE

SIMONE, APPARENTLY, TOM. PROBABLY NOT HER REAL NAME...JUST THE ONE SHE USES ON BABESTATION...

SHE'S MY CROUPIER

AND HERE'S THE CLEVER BIT, TOM. EVERY TIME SHE LEANS FORWARD TO PUT THE CHIPS ON, HER TITS NEARLY FALL OUT...NOT QUITE, BUT NEARLY

GIGGLE!

SEE?

AND THE PUNTERS KEEP BETTING IN THE HOPE THAT THE **NEXT** SPIN IS THE ONE WHERE THE PUPPIES JUMP OUT OF THE BAG...

STANDARD PRACTICE IN VEGAS, TOM

NOT ONLY THAT, WHILE THEY'RE ALL LOOKING AT HER TITS, YOURS TRULY CAN POP THE BALL IN ANY SLOT IN THE WHEEL...

WELL, THEY'LL ALL BE LOOKING AT HER TITS AS WELL, TOM

...OOH! WELL I NEVER! ZERO AGAIN!...HOUSE WINS.

YOU CAN'T DO **THAT**, ROGER. THE REGULATORS KEEP A CLOSE EYE ON TELEVISION GAMBLING

NO, ROGER. YOU HAVE TO SPIN THE WHEEL **FAIRLY!** THE BALL LANDS WHERE IT LANDS

I'M WITH YOU, TOM...METAL BALL, IS IT?

WHAT?

MAGNET UNDER THE ZERO, SOMETHING LIKE THAT?

NO! **NOTHING** LIKE THAT

OH!?...30 SECOND DELAY IN TRANS-MISSION, EH?

ONCE WE KNOW THE RESULT WE CAN SCREEN OUT WINNING BETS...NICE AND SIMPLE.

NO!

NO!

NO!

ALL THE TRAPS TOO SMALL EXCEPT ZERO!

CGI BALL AND GREENSCREEN?

FOR **GOD'S SAKE**, ROGER!

ARE *YOU* A TV PRODUCER? Are you stuck for ideas? If the answer to the first question is yes, then let's face it, your answer to the second question is going to be the same.

You know the scene - you're sitting in the boardroom trying to come up with a sure-fire ratings blockbuster for the autumn schedule. But all that is going through your mind is the scene from *I'm Alan Partridge* where he suggests Monkey Tennis. Well it's time to stop twiddling your thumbs and start twiddling your pencil-top as the *Viz* patent **FORMAT-O-MATIC** comes to the rescue.

HOW IS THIS POSSIBLE?

We have cracked the magic formul for getting a programme on the box an we're giving that secret to you as a gift! random twiddle of this pencil top TV pro gramme format generator will instant throw up any one of *10,000 chart-toppin shows*, every one of which is guarantee to tickle a commissioning editor's fancy

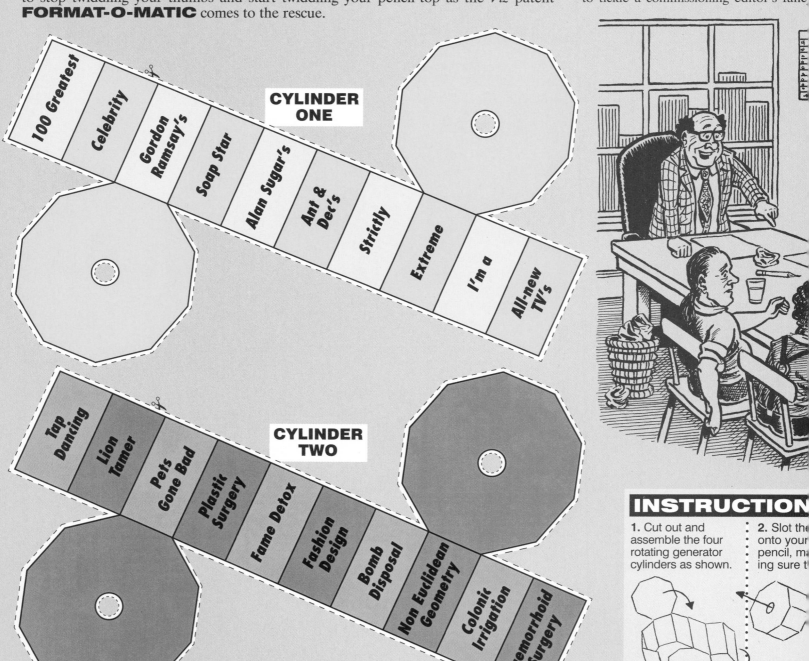

CYLINDER ONE

100 Greatest · Celebrity · Gordon Ramsay's · Soap Star · Alan Sugar's · Ant & Dec's · Strictly · Extreme · I'm a · All-new TV's

CYLINDER TWO

Tap Dancing · Lion Tamer · Pets Gone Bad · Plastic Surgery · Fame Detox · Fashion Design · Bomb Disposal · Non Euclidean Geometry · Colonic Irrigation · Haemorrhoid Surgery

INSTRUCTION

1. Cut out and assemble the four rotating generator cylinders as shown.

2. Slot the onto your pencil, ma ing sure t

RMAT-O-MATIC

rom *100 Greatest Colonic Irrigation* *oot Camp Nightmares*, to *Celebrity Lion* *mer Sex Academy on Ice*. From *Gordon* *amsay's Pets Gone Bad Gender Swap* *ove Island*, to *Extreme Fashion Design* *ospice From Hell* - hit show formats will *ow* effortlessly from your pencil, and all *re* guaranteed to be as imaginative as *nything* you see on telly these days.

TURBO-CHARGE YOUR BRAINSTORMING SESSIONS WITH A 4-CYLINDER IDEA ENGINE!

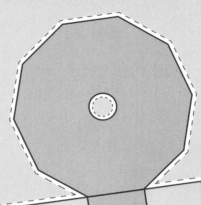

CYLINDER THREE

Funeral Parlour | Boardroom | Gender Swap | Weddings | Boot Camp | Sex Academy | Neighbours | Kitchen | Hospice | Jungle

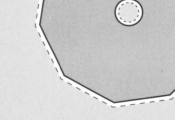

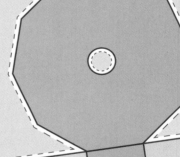

Naughtiest Blunders | 's Little Brother | TV Moments | Nightmares | Idol | Love Island | Get Me Out of Here | Love Island | From Hell | On Ice

the *ct order* *,4, left* *ht).*

3. During a meeting, twiddle with the cylinders and astonish the commissioning editor with your torrent of creative ideas.

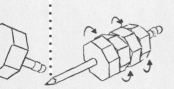

CYLINDER FOUR

"My entire Autumn schedule took under a minute to come up with. Thanks, Format-o-matic!"
Mr D Liddiment, ITV

"The Format-o-matic comes up with nothing but repetitive, half-arsed, unimaginative ideas. It's putting me out of business."
P Bazalgette, London

"I have never had a creative thought in my entire life, but thanks to the Viz Format-o-matic, I'm head of prime-time programming at a major British broadcasting corporation."
M Thompson, Broadcasting House

"If I was still in charge of the BBC, I would pay £1million pounds of licence payers' money for any of the shows generated by the Viz Format-o-matic, and that's a promise. But I'm not."
G Dyke, Brentford

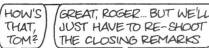

ONE DAY...

HI, ROGER!

HI, TOM

WELCOME BACK...

HOW WAS INDIA?

ABSOLUTELY SHOCKING, TOM... I'VE NEVER SEEN ANYTHING LIKE IT!... THE SWEATSHOPS... I MUST HAVE GONE TO SEE DOZENS OF 'EM...

CHRIST...

LITTLE KIDDIES, TOM, WORKING 18 HOURS A DAY FOR A BOWL OF RICE

SLAVE LABOUR, TOM, THAT'S WHAT IT IS... NO OTHER WORD FOR IT.

TCHOH! SOUNDS AWFUL, ROGER

HMM

NO HEALTH AND SAFETY... NO SICK PAY... NO HOLIDAYS... NOWT

DON'T EVEN GET A BREAK FOR LUNCH, TOM... CAN YOU BELIEVE IT?

IT'S HOW THEY MAKE THE STUFF SO CHEAP, I SUPPOSE

DEAR, OH DEAR. WHEN DOES IT GO OUT, ROGER?

WHEN DOES WHAT GO OUT, TOM?

THE DOCUMENTARY

WHAT DOCUMENTARY'S THAT?

YOUR DOCUMENTARY, ROGER! YOUR EXPOSÉ OF THE SWEATSHOPS OF INDIA...

GOD, NO...

I WASN'T MAKING A FILM, TOM. ANYWAY, THAT SUBJECT'S BEEN DONE TO FUCKIN' DEATH!

...NO, I WAS OUT THERE GETTING A FEW QUOTES FOR MY NEW RANGE OF LEISUREWEAR...

WHAT DO YOU RECKON TO THESE?

PLACE IN BANGALORE CAN DO 'EM FOR FIVE PENCE A UNIT, TOM... FIVE PENCE! AND I CAN KNOCK THE FUCKERS OUT FOR THE THICK END OF THIRTY QUID!

I ♥ RM

Zeppo Club

HOMELESS AND EAR BITTEN OFF. ALAN DAVIES

HI, ROGER. JUST HAD AN AD AGENCY ON THE PHONE... WANT YOU TO DO A VOICEOVER

SMASHING... WHAT FOR?

...VW? GUINESS? HSBC?

MENTAL MICKEY'S REMNANT WORLD ON THE TRADING ESTATE

THEIR MONEY'S AS GOOD AS ANY FUCKER'S, TOM

WHEN DO THEY WANT ME IN?

SORRY, TOM. CAN'T DO IT.

THE STUDIO IS BOOKED FOR WEDNESDAY

...I'M UP BEFORE THE BEAK ON WEDNESDAY

OH, NO, NOT AGAIN, ROGER... WHAT IS IT THIS TIME?

IT'S AN "HISTORICAL" SEX OFFENCE, TOM.

OH, GOD... I ALWAYS KNEW YOU'D START PAYING ONE DAY FOR THE WAY YOU BEHAVED IN THE SEVENTIES AND EIGHTIES, ROGER.

WHEN DID THIS ONE TAKE PLACE?

LAST WEEK, TOM

GLUG! GLUG! GLUG!

LAST WEEK!?!... BUT... BUT... I THOUGHT YOU SAID IT WAS AN HISTORICAL OFFENCE

THAT'S RIGHT...

...I WAS FILMING A DOCUMENTARY ABOUT HENRY THE EIGHTH AT THE TOWER OF LONDON, AND I MADE A BIT OF A GRAB FOR THAT LUCY WORSLEY'S TITS

ROGER MELLIE
the man on the telly

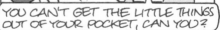

...I CAN'T READ A BLOODY **THING** WITHOUT THEM... FULLY..SOMETHING OR OTHER...

WHERE ARE THEY?

HERE THEY ARE, ROGER

THANKS... OH, **NO**!.. THEY'RE MY **DRIVERS**... I NEED MY **READERS**...

I'VE HAD 'EM TODAY... WHERE THE **FUCK**..?

HERE THEY ARE

GREAT...RIGHT... THIS IS 'FULLY-LOADED CLIP' BY FIVE-NOUGHT CENT...

...NEVER HEARD OF THEM

YOU WANN' PROBLEM WIT ME! NO PROBLEM. IT'S ALL GOOD! I AIN'T FRESH OUT THE HOOD! I'M STILL IN THE HOOD!

THE CONTROLLER WOULD LIKE A WORD AFTER THE SHOW, ROGER

RIGHT-HO, TOM

SHORTLY...

ROGER!.. NICE TO SEE YOU. COME IN... SIT DOWN

OKAY...LOOK, ROGER... I THINK WE BOTH KNOW IT'S TIME TO MAKE SOME CHANGES ON THE BREAKFAST SHOW...

YOU'RE TELLING **ME**!..

...THAT FUCKING POSSE IS NEXT TO **USELESS**! I TRIED TO GET THAT BIT GOING ABOUT THE COOKIE BEAR ON THE ANDY WILLIAMS SHOW AND THEY JUST LOOKED FUCKING **BLANK**!

NO, ROGER...

...IT'S **YOU**! YOU'RE SIMPLY NOT SPEAKING TO OUR TARGET DEMOGRAPHIC OF 15-22 YEAR-OLDS

EH!?

THEY DON'T KNOW WHAT YOU'RE TALKING ABOUT SOME OF THE TIME. WELL, **MOST** OF THE TIME, ACTUALLY. I'M BRINGING IN A NEW, YOUNGER PRESENTER FOR THE BREAKFAST SHOW

I'VE ARRANGED A TRANSFER FOR YOU TO THE SUNDAY MORNING SLOT ON OUR SISTER STATION, **SENIOR F.M.**

SENIOR FUCKING F.M.? TELL ME YOU'RE JOKING

YOU'LL BE **GREAT**!

NO I **WON'T**! CHATTING ON TO A LOAD OF OLD FUCKING COFFIN DODGERS...**ME**?

WELL THE AUDIENCE **ARE** MORE MATURE, ROGER, BUT I THINK YOU'LL GO DOWN WELL

YOUR BLEND OF GENTLE REMINISCENCE AND NOSTALGIA FOR THE OLD DAYS IS JUST WHAT THE STATION NEEDS...

...AND YOU'LL BE IN **FULL CONTROL**

YOU'LL GET TO CHOSE THE RECORDS AND INVITE YOUR OWN GUESTS ON THE SHOW

NEXT SUNDAY... WELL, THAT WAS 'I'LL REMEMBER YOU' BY FRANKIE IFIELD, AND I'M SURE WE ALL REMEMBER **HIM**! I RECALL SEEING HIM IN 1961 AT THE FULCHESTER PALAIS... SADLY NOW GONE TO MAKE WAY FOR A BRANCH OF **DALLAS CARPETS**...

...WHICH YOURS TRULY WILL BE OPENING TOMORROW...

...SO POP ALONG AT 2·00 AND SAY HELLO... PERHAPS BUY A COPY OF MY NEW BOOK...

...NOW A LITTLE SOMETHING FROM GLEN MILLER

HE'S DOING A **GREAT** JOB, ISN'T HE, TOM

YES. HE'S DONE WONDERS WITH THE FORMAT

WELL THAT WAS GLEN MILLER WITH 'STRING OF PEARLS'... A BEAUTIFUL TUNE...

...IT ALWAYS PUTS ME IN MIND OF THE FIRST PEARL NECKLACE I EVER GAVE TO MY WIFE...

AND HE HASN'T SWORN ONCE

...TONS OF THE STUFF, THERE WAS... WENT RIGHT UP HER CHIN AND EVERYTHING...

AH... HAPPY DAYS.

ANYWAY, IT'S TIME FOR "SUNDAY THOUGHT"...AND I'M PLEASED TO WELCOME A GOOD FRIEND OF MINE...

VICAR OF ST. BARDOLPHS, THE REV. PAUL WHICKER

THANK YOU, ROGER...

...NOW THESE DAYS PEOPLE OFTEN ASK ME MY POSITION ON WOMEN IN THE CHURCH...

...AND I ALWAYS ANSWER...REVERSE COWGIRL ACROSS THE ALTAR... WITH MY THUMB UP THEIR ARSE.

I've Been Ad

ONE OF THE NICE THINGS about being let into people's living rooms every night through the medium of television, is that the audience feel they actually know you. Over the years, a bond of trust develops. The best thing about this is that a celebrity can abuse this trust, endorsing any old shit in return for cash. And over the years I've endorsed more than my fair share of shit, both at home and abroad. Here are a few of my own favourites...

Walk upstairs after a skinful? ...ME? FUCK OFF!

"I've got a WINSTON Stair Lift"

says Roger Mellie OBE, star of TV's 'Opportunity Cocks'

Call FREE *NOW!*
Dial 100 and ask for

FREEPHONE WINSTON

"Fuck what Raymond Baxter and Thora Hird say, all other stairlifts are a load of fucking shit" Roger Mellie OBE

BRITISH MADE

"I got forty grand up front for this one. And a free stairlift. Though I must confess, I wasn't their first choice. My old pal Ollie Reed was already lined up for the gig, but fortunately he kicked the bucket and I was in like a rat up a fucking drainpipe. One photo, one signature, one Ferrari. Ten minutes! Life doesn't come better than that."

"Here's yours truly doing his bit to help British exports. Some people might criticise me for doing this ad, but what these lefties don't understand is that I got paid 80 fucking grand in a suitcase. I can see that torture equipment might not be everyone's cup of tea, but the workmanship of the stuff was first rate."

La Estrella Británica famosa, Roger Mellie, ordenador principal de la televisión "Up Your Cunt" y "Fuck a Duck" del recomienda siempre el equipo de la tortura fabricado por

Anglo-Fulchester Light Engineering.

"Con un rango tan extensoa elegir de, el Anglo-Fulchester es su opción de una parada el dictador del crisol de la lata de hoy" exclaimas Roger.

Británicos fabricación!

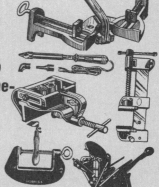

- Alojamientos de la mano.
- Grillos de la pierna.
- Bastones de mando de alto voltaje del control de la muchedumbre.
- Alicates del testículos.
- Vice del pene.
- Puntas de prueba anales eléctricas.

'Concesión de la Reina para las Exportaciones Barbáricas e Inhumanes' 1982

TODO EL PAPELEO FALSIFICADO EN LA CONSULTA CON LA OFICINA NO NATIVA!!

Oficinas Regionales - Chile, Beijing, Indonesia, la Arabia Saudita

I bet HE drinks Carling Black Label.

"This was part of the famous lager campaign of the 80s. I was a bit nervous before the shoot because, to be honest, I'd only ever shagged five birds in a row before, (backstage at a Spice Girls concert), so I was entering unknown territory. But I rose to the occasion magnificently, though I say so myself. Then, would you believe it, the clients lost their bottle and pulled the ad. But it paid for my third divorce so who gives a fuck."

"Like any celeb worth his salt, I get pulled for DD every year. Except for 1975, when I did this poster for the local fuzz. In return for me doing the ad, they agreed to look the other way when I drove out the pub car park, just like they do for the Chief Constable. Best Christmas I ever had."

"This is a very early advert from when I first shot to fame doing 'Last Turkey in the Shop' on Saturday Night at the London Palladium, filling in for Bruce Forsyth who'd had a bad curry and was shitting fizzy gravy in his dressing room. When I did the ad, they gave me a free sample, which I lent to Frank Muir. It fused during his vinegar strokes and gave the poor sod a 240v belt up his hog's eye. Or was it Eamonn Andrews?"

ROGER MELLIE
THE MAN ON THE TELLY

HI, THERE, REX. SORRY I'M A TAD LATE

A TWO HOUR AND TWENTY MINUTE TAD TO BE PRECISE, ROGER...

STILL, YOU'RE HERE NOW, SO LETS GET ON WITH THE MEETING.

CUP OF COFFEE PLEASE, LOVE. THREE SUGARS

OKAY, ROGER

I'VE HAD A CHANCE TO GO THROUGH YOUR AUTOBIOGRAPHY... 'JOLLY ROGER - A LIFE ON THE TELLY'

THAT'S GREAT

AND, ERM...

NOW, I WANT HALF A MILLION NON-RETURNABLE ADVANCE UP FRONT, PLUS 20% OF THE COVER PRICE OF EVERY COPY PRINTED...

...THAT'S PRINTED, REX, NOT SHIFTED!

ROGER...

...NO DISCOUNTS FOR BULK, NEITHER. IF TESCO OR ASDA OR THE LIKE START NEGOTIATING THE PRICE DOWN, TELL 'EM TO FUCK OFF, REX.

CHEEKY BASTARDS!

...AND NO SALE OR RETURN, EITHER

...OKAY!?

...NONE!

ROGER...

ROGER...

REX WINDARSE PUBLISHING

I DON'T WANT YOU TURNING UP ON BOXING DAY WANTING HALF YOUR WEDGE BACK BECAUSE BORDERS HAVE GOT A SKIPFULL OF THE FUCKERS LEFT OVER...

...THEY BUY 'EM...THEY'RE BOUGHT!

RIGHT!.. TRANSLATION RIGHTS, TALKING BOOKS, LARGE PRINT, AND BRAILLE EDITIONS...I WANT 60% OF THE...

IF I CAN STOP YOU THERE, ROGER.

...I'M AFRAID WE'RE NOT GOING TO PUBLISH IT IN THAT FORM...

...IT JUST WON'T BE A BIG ENOUGH SELLER.

WHAT!?! WHAT DO YOU MEAN!? IT'S A CELEBRITY BIOGRAPHY, REX...YOU CAN'T MOVE FOR THE FUCKERS IN BOOKSHOPS THIS YEAR...IT'S A SURE FIRE WINNER

EVERYONE IN THE BIZ IS AT IT... RICHARD MADELEY, FERN BRITTON, THAT COMEDIENNE WOMAN...Y'KNOW...THAT... BLOODY FAT VICAR ONE. WOTSERNAME

YES, I KNOW ROGER, BUT...

200 PAGES OF TOP CELEB ANECDOTES, THAT... PLUS 16 PAGES OF PHOTOS OF ME AND BRUCIE PLAYING GOLF

YES, BUT...

AND LOADS OF ME BEING INTRODUCED TO HER MAJ AT THE ROYAL VARIETY SHOW

BUT THERE'S THE PROBLEM, ROGER

WHAT?

THAT TIRED SHOWBIZ AUTOBIOGRAPHY FORMAT WENT OUT YEARS AGO...

NOBODY THESE DAYS CARES ABOUT THE LORDS TAVERNERS, OR THE WATER RATS, OR STORIES ABOUT YOU CATCHING TARBY IN TERRY-THOMAS'S DRESSING ROOM.

THE PUBLIC WANT CELEBS MEMOIRS THESE DAYS.

MEMOIRS?

YOU KNOW...DEPRIVED CHILDHOOD, ALCOHOL AND DRUG ABUSE...

...HOLLOW TRAPPINGS OF SUCCESS, CAREER SETBACKS, NERVOUS BREAKDOWNS... THAT SORT OF THING

I SEE!

DID YOUR DAD EVER BEAT YOU

ROGER MELLIE

THE MAN ON THE TELLY

4.00 am. AT TOM, THE DIRECTOR'S HOUSE...

ZZZZ!

DRING! DRING!! DRING! DRING!!

EH!?...WASSAT!?

ER...ERM... HELLO!?

ROGER! DO YOU KNOW WHAT TIME IT IS?

WHAT THE HELL DO YOU WANT?

I'M IN TROUBLE, TOM. BIG TROUBLE

GOD! WHAT'S HAPPENED, ROGER?

ARE YOU IN PRISON OR SOMETHING?

WORSE THAN THAT, TOM... THEY'VE PUT ME IN THE FUCKIN' SAUCE CLINIC

I'M FACING UP TO IT, TOM. I'VE GOT A PROBLEM, BUT I CAN'T DO IT ON MY OWN. I NEED YOUR HELP... YOUR SUPPORT. PLEASE

DON'T WORRY, ROGER. I'LL BE OVER FIRST THING IN THE MORNING. YOU CAN RELY ON ME

THANKS, TOM. THAT'S GREAT. WE'LL HAVE A CHAT... SORT THIS THING OUT, ONCE AND FOR ALL, EH? LOOK FORWARD TO SEEING YOU...

...OH, JUST ONE THING, TOM...

DO ME A FAVOUR AND BRING A BOTTLE OF KETCHUP IN Y' POCKET, WILL YOU?

...I'M FUCKIN' CHOKIN' FOR A DRINK

NEXT MORNING...

WELCOME TO THE BETTY FORD-CAPRI CLINIC FOR PISSED UP CELEBS £3000 per WEEK

...AND THIS IS ME! BLOOAGH!

HI, ROGER. NICE TO SEE YOU. HOW ARE YOU FEE...

FUCK THE SMALLTALK, TOM. COME ON, LET THE DOG SEE THE RABBIT

WOR! THANKS, TOM, EH! I KNEW I COULD COUNT ON YOU. LET ME NECK THIS TWAT FIRST, EH? WE CAN HAVE A CHIN WAG LATER. THANKS AGAIN, MATE.

EH!? YOU FUCKING CUNT... WHAT'S THIS?

SORRY, ROGER. BUT IT'S FOR YOUR OWN GOOD

YOU'RE HERE TO DRY OUT

NO... THE DOCTOR SAID I COULD HAVE ONE OR TWO... HONEST.. FOR MY BREAKFAST... JUST TO GET ME GOING

LOOK, ROGER. THE FIRST STEP ON THE ROAD TO RECOVERY IS ADMITTING YOU'VE GOT A PROBLEM

OH, I ADMIT THERE'S A PROBLEM, TOM... THREE FUCKIN' GRAND A WEEK AND THIS PLACE HASN'T EVEN GOT A BAR!..

THAT'S THE PROBLEM

I MEAN, FUCK ME, TOM, EVERYONE IN T.V. LIKES THEIR POP. IT GOES WITH THE TERRITORY

YOU SHOW ME A T.V. PERSONALITY WHO DOESN'T NUDGE THE TURPS AND I'LL SHOW YOU A LYING CUNT

BUT I'M A PRO TOM. I DON'T LET IT INTERFERE WITH MY WORK

OH, NO? WHAT ABOUT THE 50 TAKES TO SAY 'HELLO, GOOD EVENING AND WELCOME?'

A CASE IN POINT, TOM. WE GOT IT IN THE CAN EVENTUALLY.

YEH! BUT IT TOOK 20 MINUTES AND THE SHOW WAS GOING OUT LIVE!

I CAN'T HELP BEING A PERFECTIONIST

ROGER! YOUR EYES ARE GLAZED, YOUR SPEECH IS SLURRED, AND YOU SHAKE VISIBLY IN FRONT OF CAMERA

WELL, WHAT'S THE FUCKIN' P.R DEPARTMENT FOR? PUT IT OUT I'VE GOT PARKINSON'S DISEASE OR SOMETHING, I DON'T KNOW...

JUST GET ME A FUCKIN' DRINK!

NO, ROGER. I CAN'T HELP YOU THERE. NO ONE CAN HELP YOU UNTIL YOU FIRST HELP YOURSELF

YOU'RE RIGHT, TOM...

I NEED TO HELP MYSELF... AND THAT'S WHAT I'M GOING TO DO

COME ON, TOM. LET'S GO BACK TO MY ROOM AND CRACK OPEN A BOTTLE OF LUCOZADE, EH?

HA! HA! HA! THAT'S MORE LIKE IT, ROGER

SHORTLY...

TIME FOR YOUR LETTUCE AND CELERY ENEMA MR. MELLIE

KNOCK! KNOCK!

EEEK!

GNNNGH! GNNGH!

MEANWHILE, AT A NEARBY OFF LICENSE...

QUICK!..

...GIMME A BOTTLE OF THE NEAREST THING TO YOU... AND A FUNNEL